FOR ORGANS, PIANOS & ELECTRONIC KEYBOARDS

16

C000296964

Exclusive Distributors:
Music Sales Limited
8/9 Frith Street, London W1V 5TZ, England.
Music Sales Pty Limited
120 Rothschild Avenue, Rosebery, NSW 2018, Australia.

Order No. HLE90000187
ISBN 0-7119-6425-4

Cover design by Pearce Marchbank, Studio Twenty, London
Printed in the USA

BROADWAY GREATS

Your Guarantee of Quality
As publishers, we strive to produce every book to
the highest commercial standards.
This book has been carefully designed to minimise awkward
page turns and to make playing from it a real pleasure.
Throughout, the printing and binding have been planned
to ensure a sturdy, attractive publication which should
give years of enjoyment.
If your copy fails to meet our high standards,
please inform us and we will gladly replace it.

Music Sales' complete catalogue describes thousands of titles
and is available in full colour sections by subject, direct from
Music Sales Limited. Please state your areas of interest and
send a cheque/postal order for £1.50 for postage to:
Music Sales Limited, Newmarket Road, Bury St. Edmunds,
Suffolk IP33 3YB, England.

Visit the Internet Music Shop at
http//www.musicsales.co.uk

Hal Leonard Europe
Distributed by Music Sales

All I Ask of You
from THE PHANTOM OF THE OPERA

Registration 8
Rhythm: 8 Beat or Rock

Music by Andrew Lloyd Webber
Lyrics by Charles Hart
Additional Lyrics by Richard Stilgoe

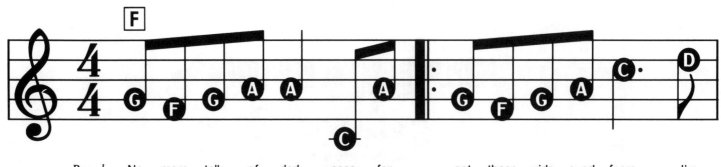

Raoul: No more talk of dark - ness, for - get these wide - eyed fears: I'm
let me be your light; you're

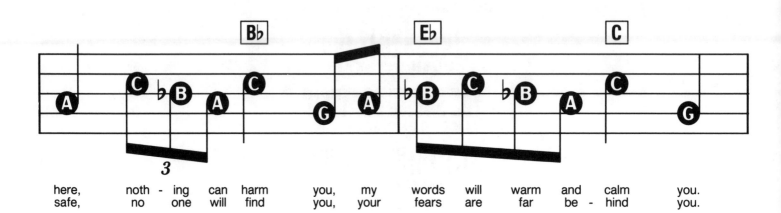

here, noth - ing can harm you, my words will warm and calm you.
safe, no one will find you, your fears are far be - hind you.

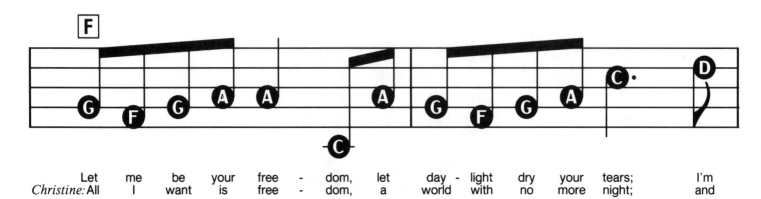

Let me be your free - dom, let day - light dry your tears; I'm
Christine: All I want is free - dom, a world with no more night; and

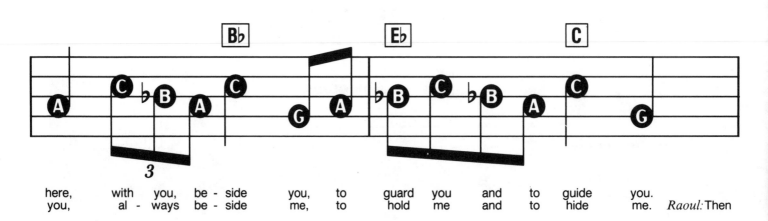

here, with you, be - side you, to guard you and to guide you.
you, al - ways be - side me, to hold me and to hide me. *Raoul:* Then

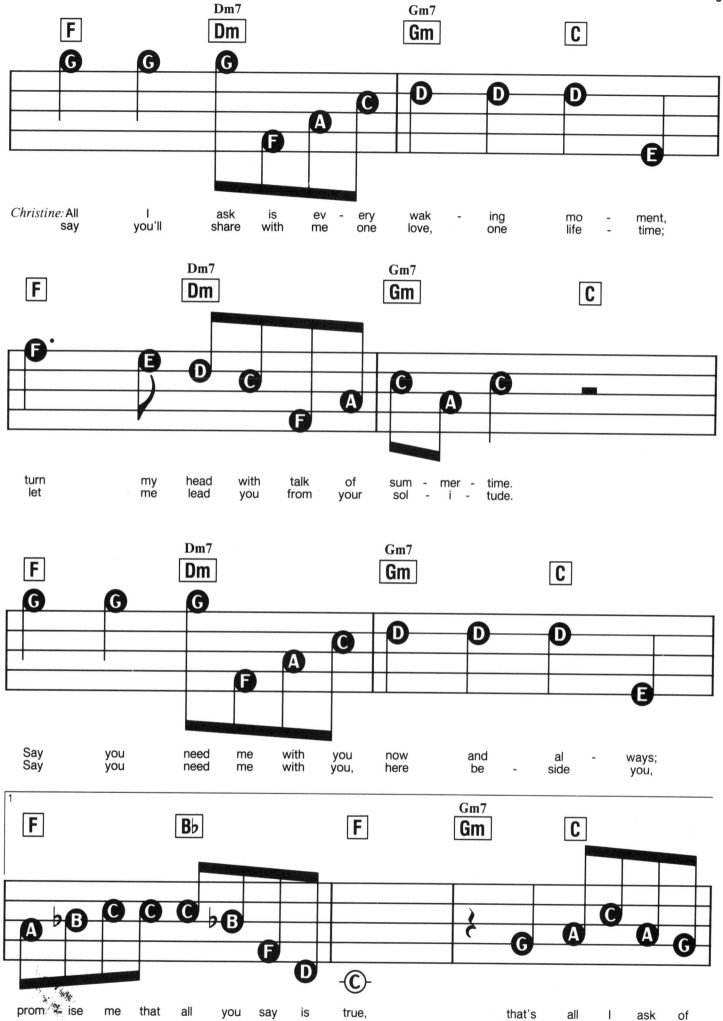

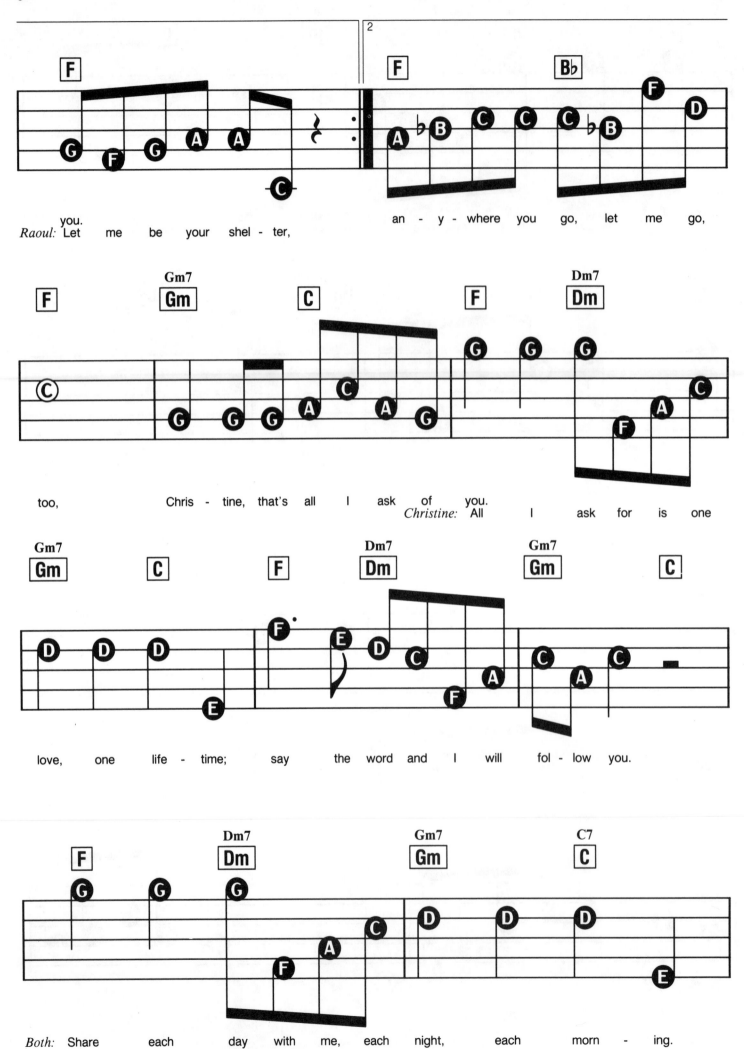

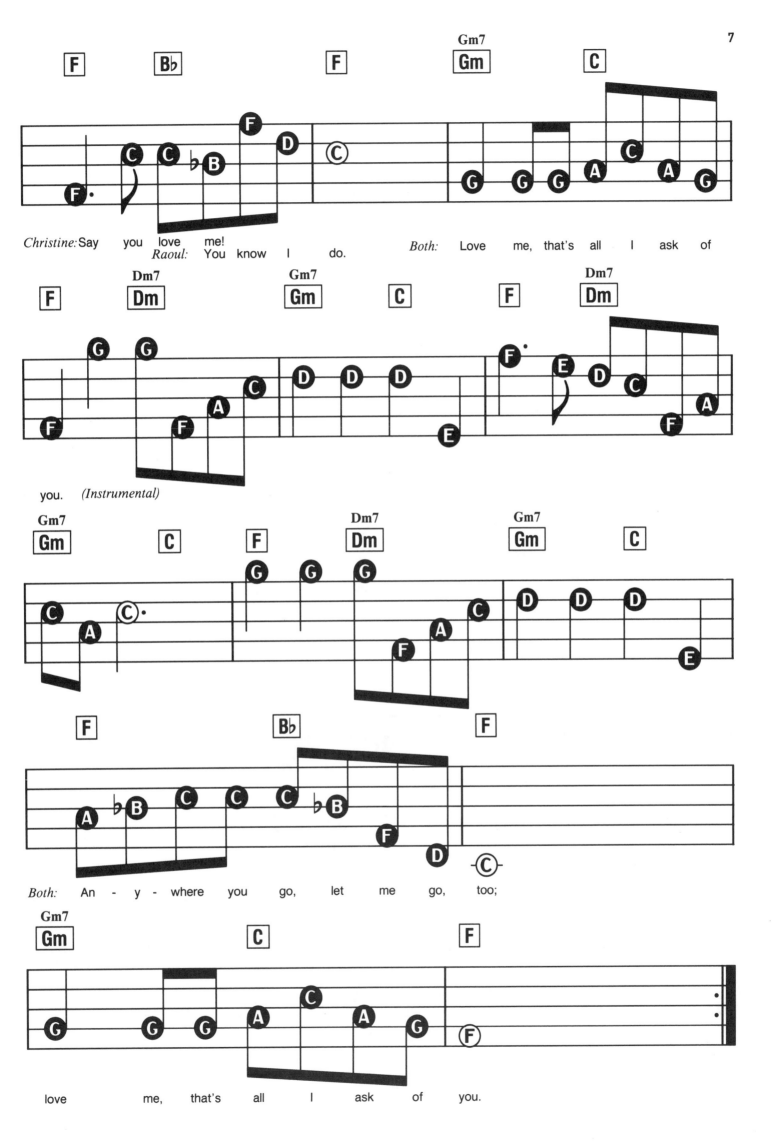

Consider Yourself

from the Columbia Pictures - Romulus film OLIVER!

Registration 2
Rhythm: 6/8 March

Words and Music by
Lionel Bart

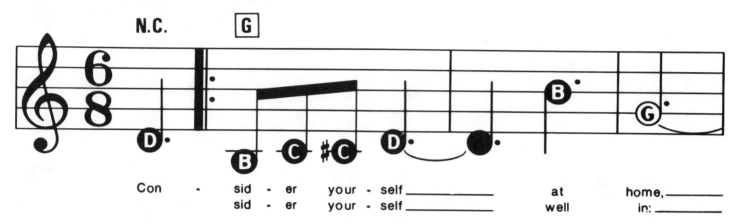

Con - sid - er your - self _____ at home, _____
sid - er your - self _____ well in: _____

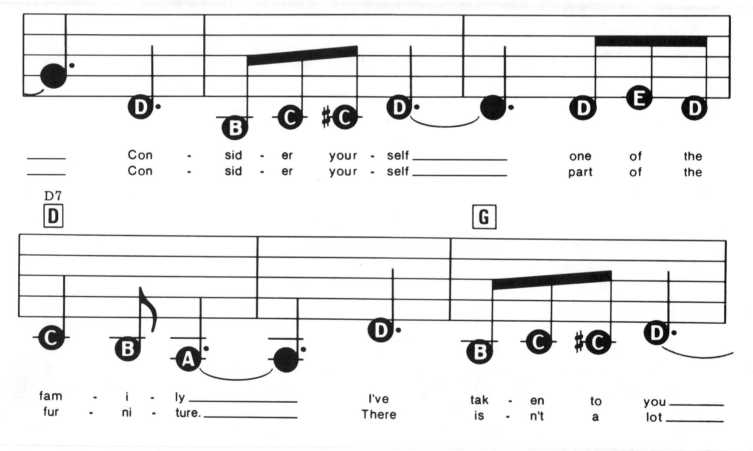

_____ Con - sid - er your - self _____ one of the
_____ Con - sid - er your - self _____ part of the

fam - i - ly _____ I've tak - en to you _____
fur - ni - ture. _____ There is - n't a lot _____

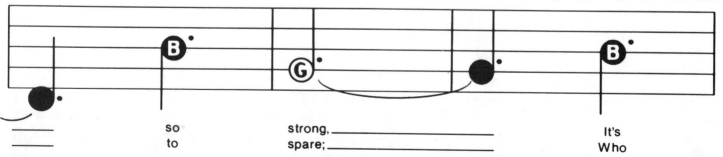

so strong, _____ It's
to spare; _____ Who

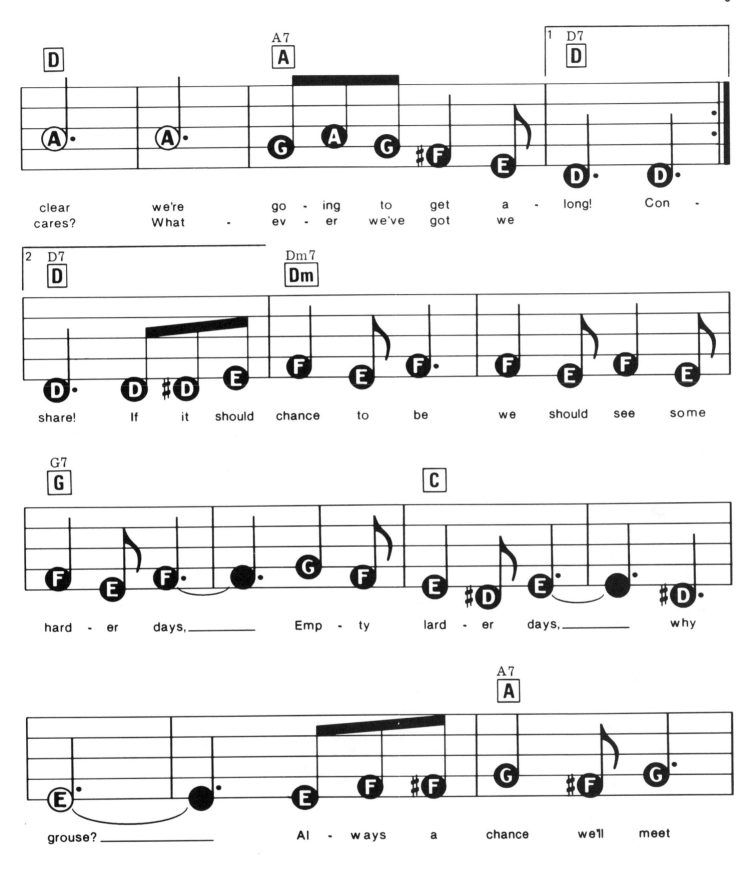

clear   we're   go - ing   to   get   a - long!   Con -
cares?   What -   ev - er   we've got   we

share!   If   it   should   chance   to   be   we   should   see   some

hard - er   days, _____   Emp - ty   lard - er   days, _____   why

grouse? _____   Al - ways   a   chance   we'll   meet

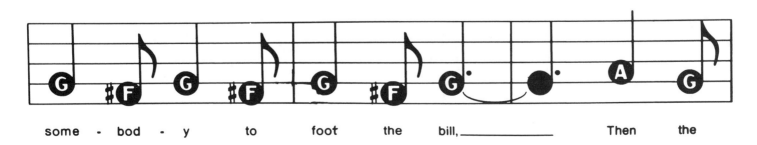

some - bod - y   to   foot   the   bill, _____   Then   the

10

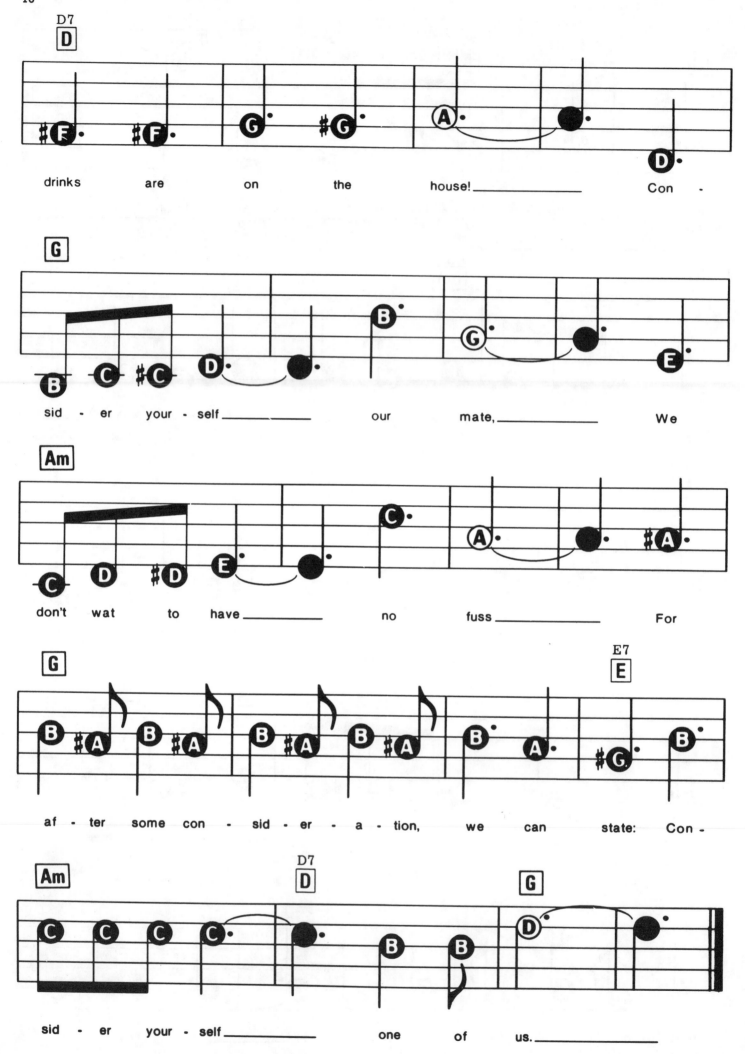

Hello, Young Lovers
from THE KING AND I

Registration 1
Rhythm: Waltz

Lyrics by Oscar Hammerstein II
Music by Richard Rodgers

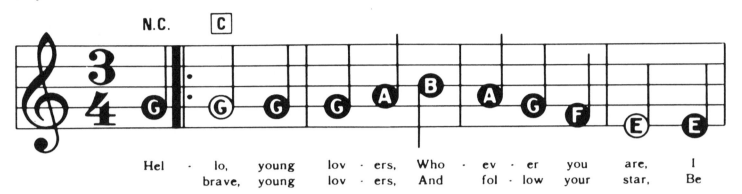

Hel - lo, young lov - ers, Who - ev - er you are, I
brave, young lov - ers, And fol - low your star, Be

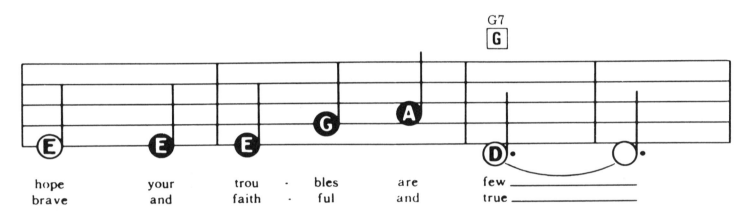

hope your trou - bles are few
brave your and faith - ful and true

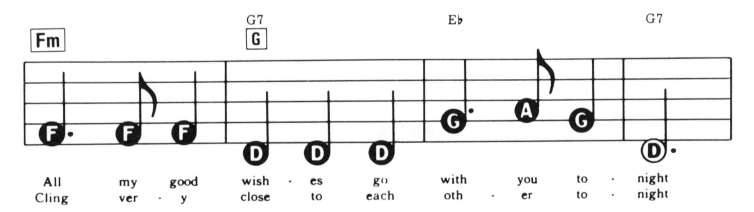

All my good wish - es go with you to - night
Cling ver - y close to each oth - er to - night

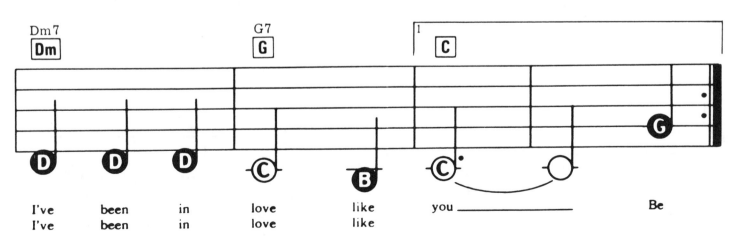

I've been in love like you
I've been in love like

Be

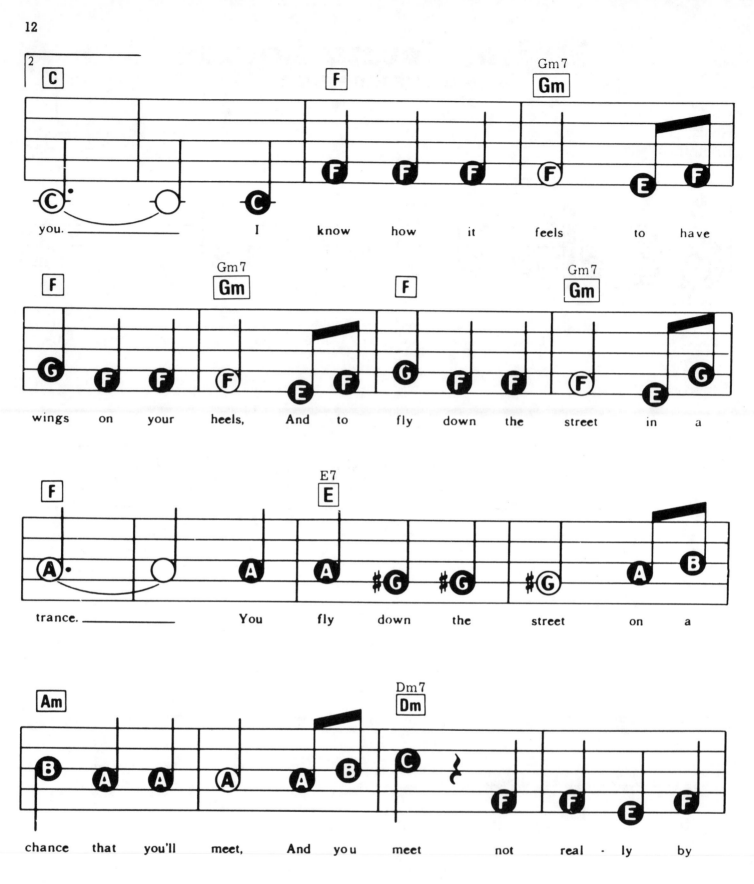

you. _____ I know how it feels to have

wings on your heels, And to fly down the street in a

trance. _____ You fly down the street on a

chance that you'll meet, And you meet not real - ly by

chance. _____ Don't cry, young lov - ers, What-

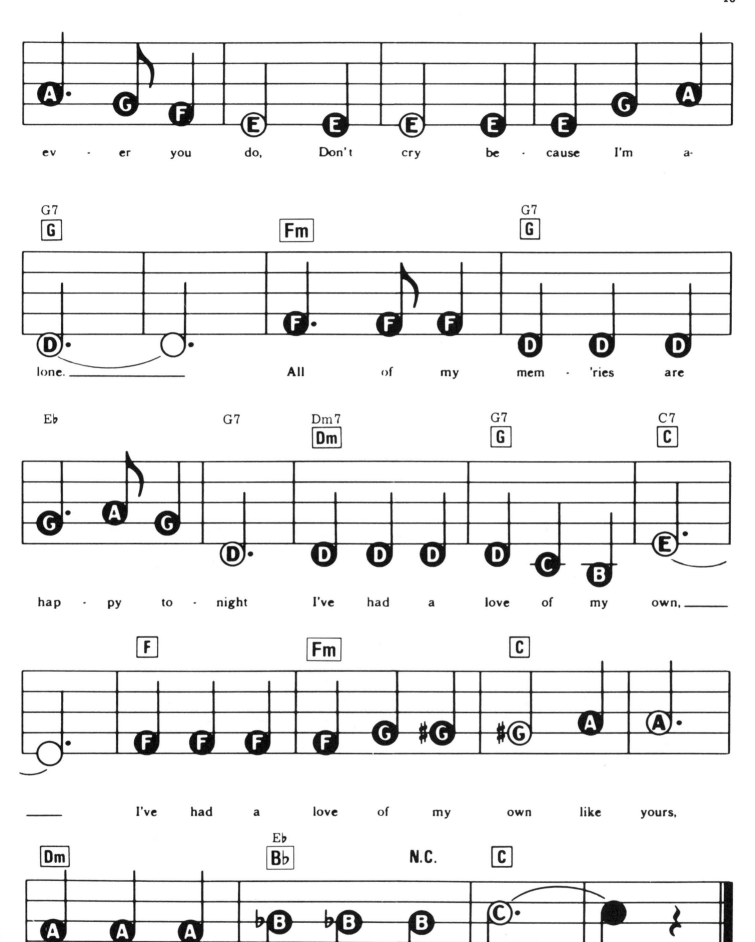

Edelweiss
from THE SOUND OF MUSIC

Registration 1
Rhythm: Waltz

Lyrics by Oscar Hammerstein II
Music by Richard Rodgers

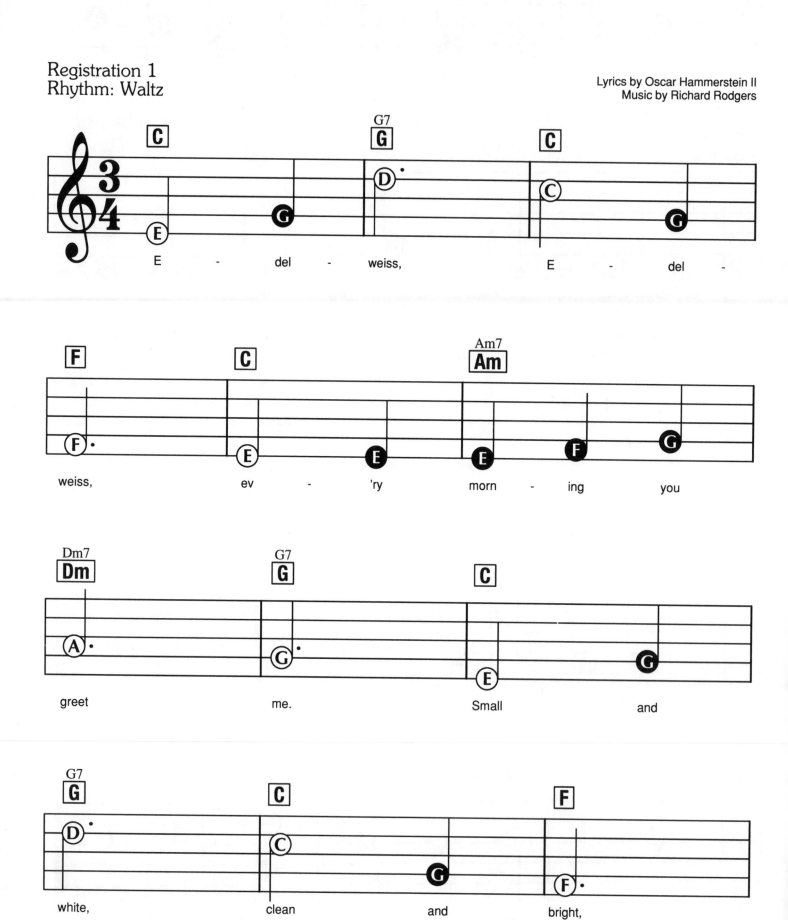

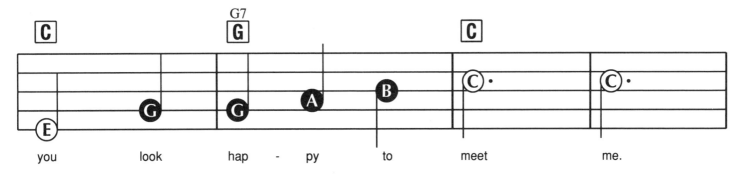

you look hap - py to meet me.

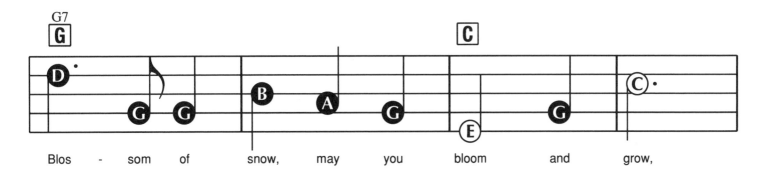

Blos - som of snow, may you bloom and grow,

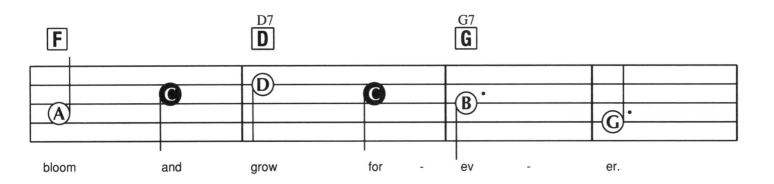

bloom and grow for - ev - er.

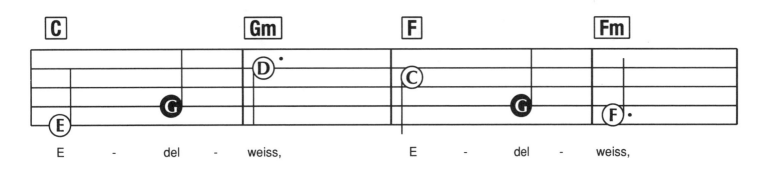

E - del - weiss, E - del - weiss,

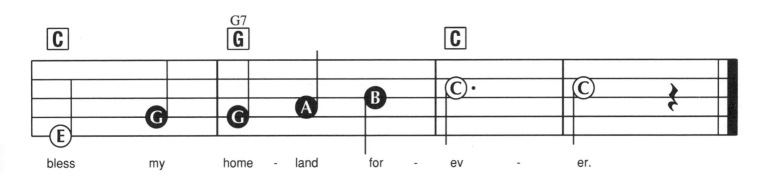

bless my home - land for - ev - er.

I Ain't Down Yet
from THE UNSINKABLE MOLLY BROWN

Registration 4
Rhythm: Polka, March or Fox Trot

Words and Music by
Meredith Willson

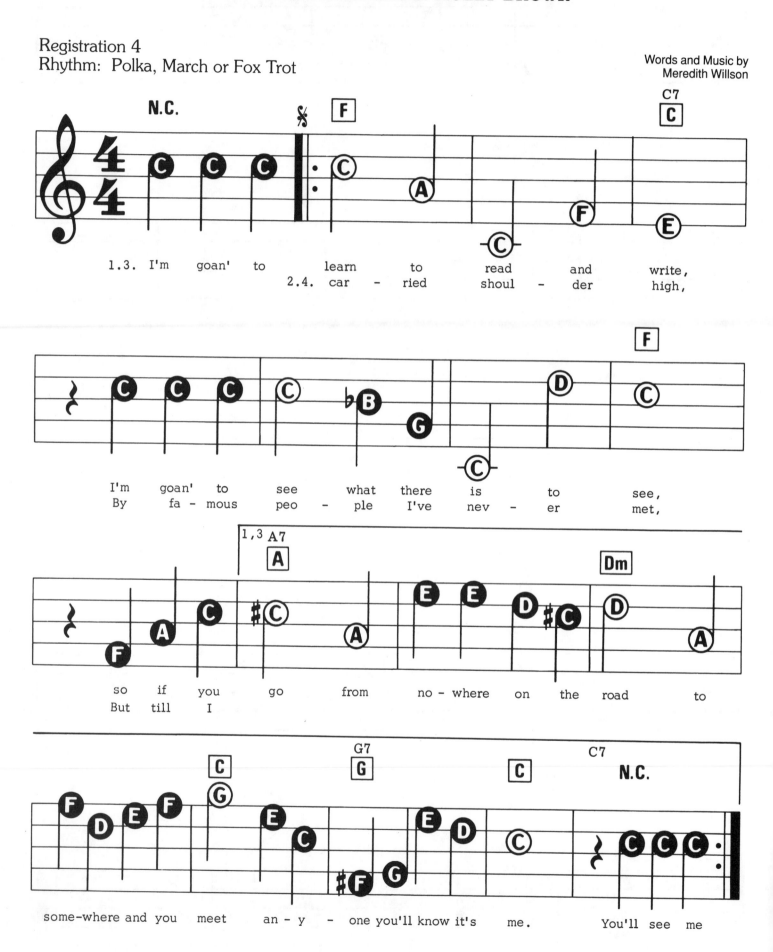

1.3. I'm goan' to learn to read and write,
2.4. car - ried shoul - der high,

I'm goan' to see what there is to see,
By fa - mous peo - ple I've nev - er met,

so if you go from no - where on the road to
But till I

some-where and you meet an - y - one you'll know it's me. You'll see me

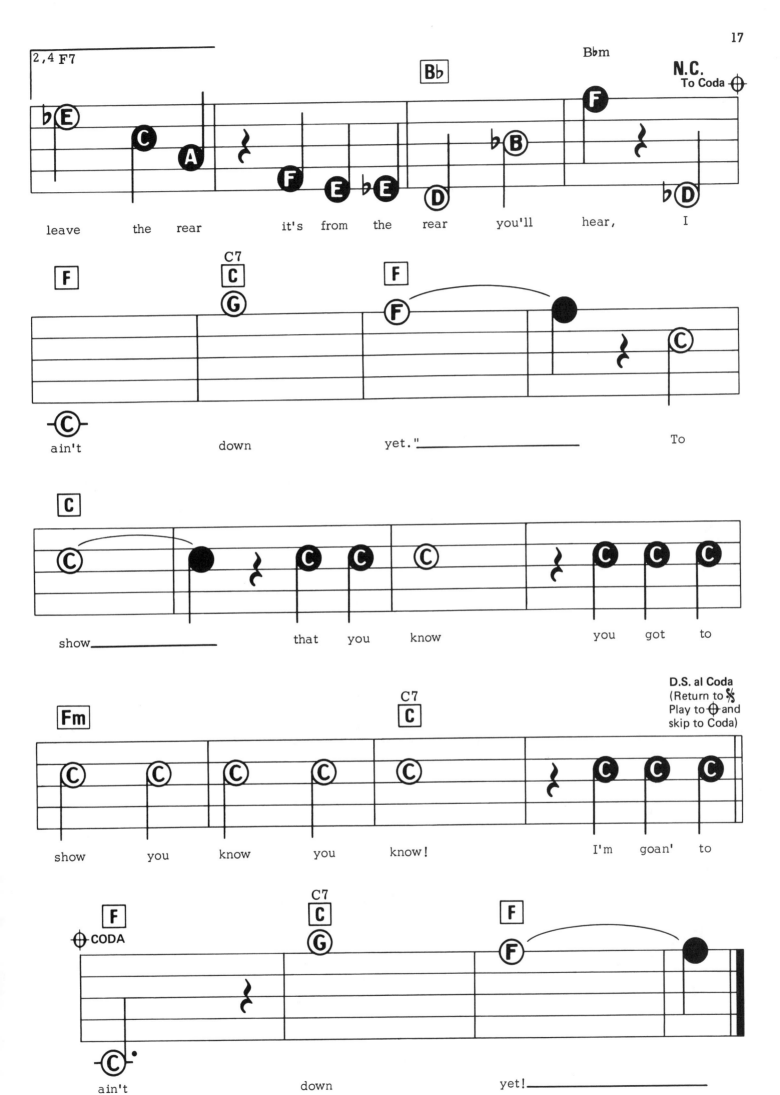

If I Were a Bell
from GUYS AND DOLLS

Registration 1
Rhythm: Fox Trot or Swing

By Frank Loesser

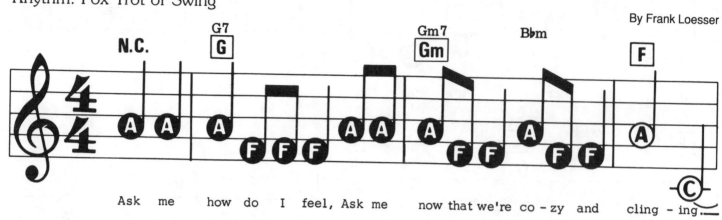

Ask me how do I feel, Ask me now that we're co-zy and cling-ing.

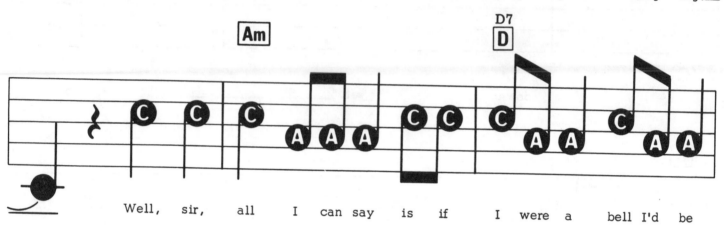

Well, sir, all I can say is if I were a bell I'd be

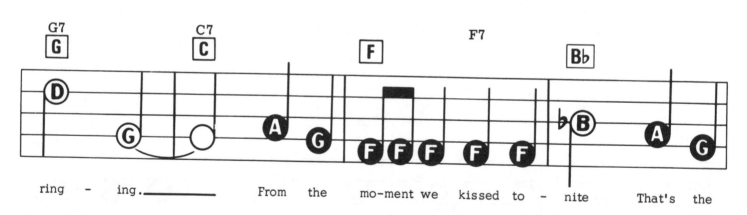

ring-ing.____ From the mo-ment we kissed to-nite That's the

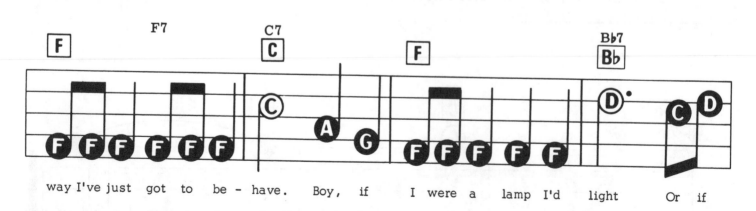

way I've just got to be-have. Boy, if I were a lamp I'd light Or if

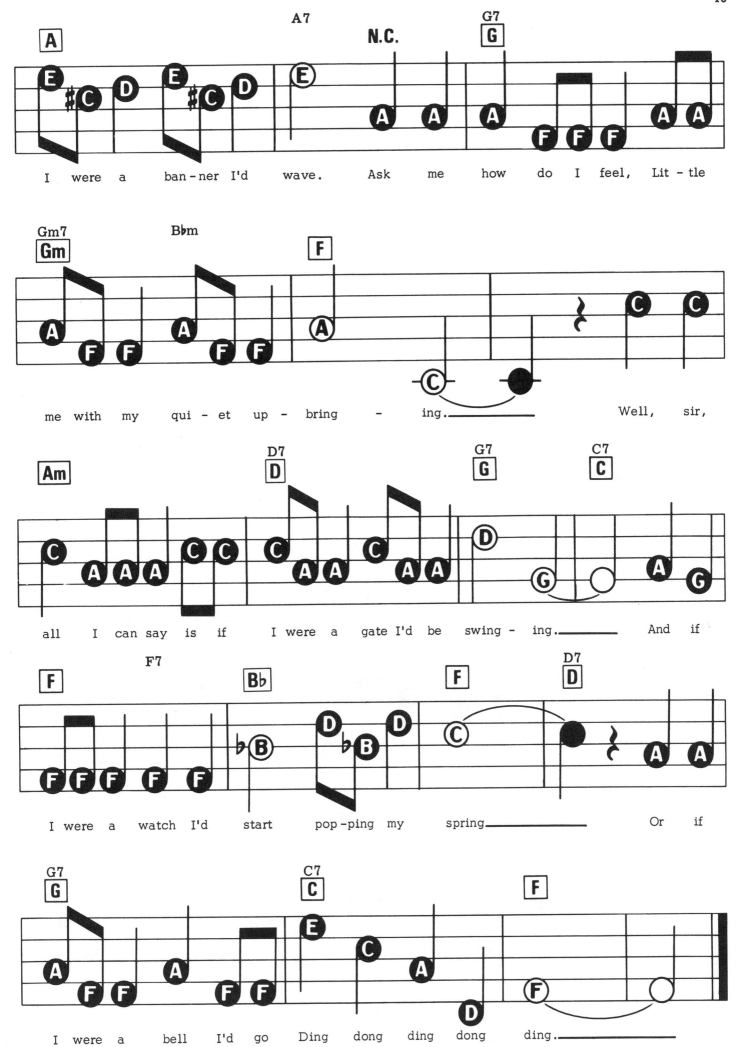

Look for the Silver Lining

from SALLY

Registration 2
Rhythm: Fox Trot or Swing

Words by Buddy DeSylva
Music by Jerome Kern

Look for ____ the sil - ver lin - ing ____

When - e'er a cloud ap - pears in the

blue. ____ Re - mem - ber some - where ____ the sun is

shin - ing ____ And so the right thing ____ to

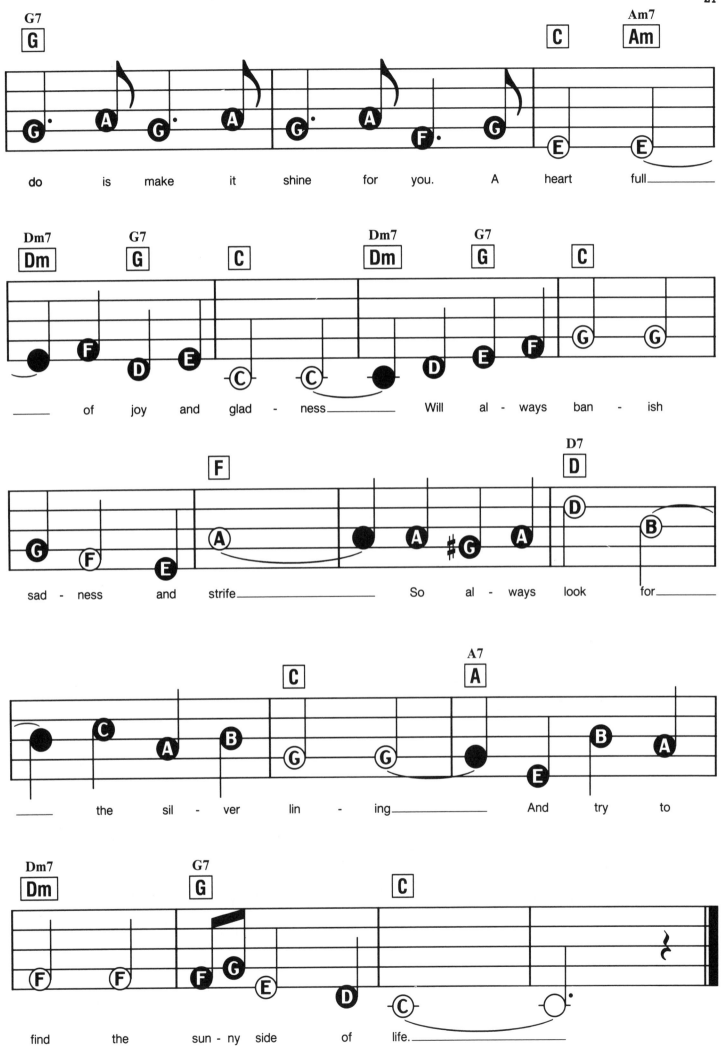

Love Changes Everything
from ASPECTS OF LOVE

Registration 2
Rhythm: Rock or 8 Beat

Music by Andrew Lloyd Webber
Lyrics by Don Black and Charles Hart

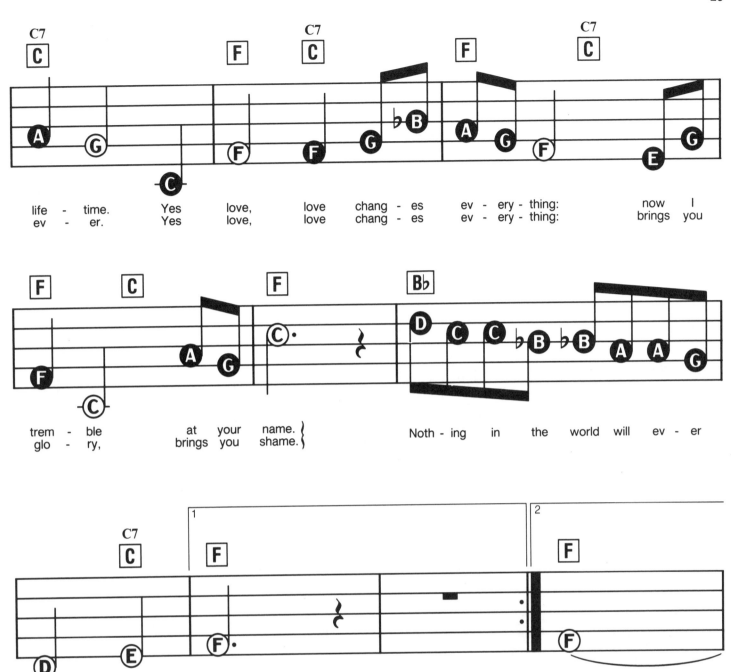

life - time. Yes love, love chang - es ev - ery - thing: now I
ev - er. Yes love, love chang - es ev - ery - thing: brings you

trem - ble at your name. } Noth - ing in the world will ev - er
glo - ry, brings you shame. }

be the same. same.

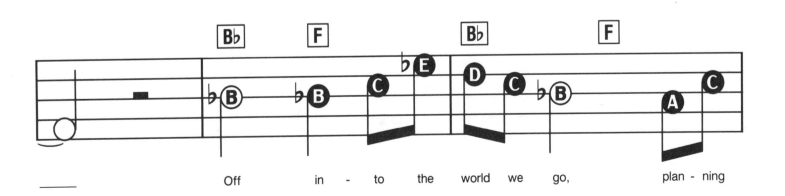

Off in - to the world we go, plan - ning

24

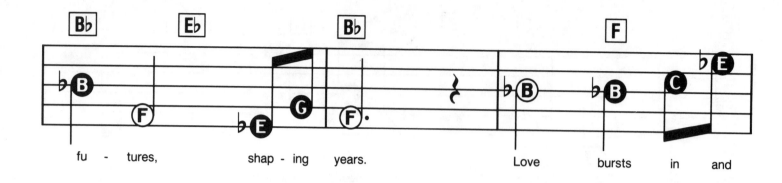

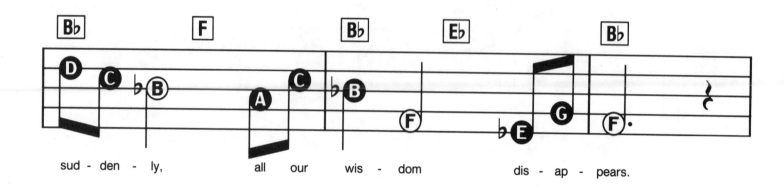

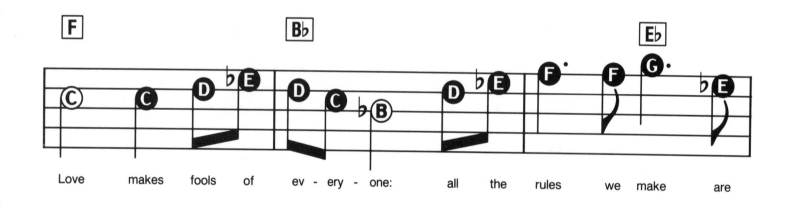

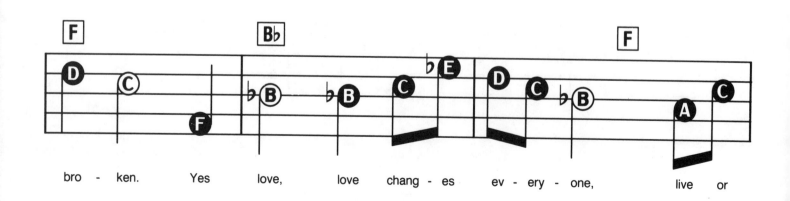

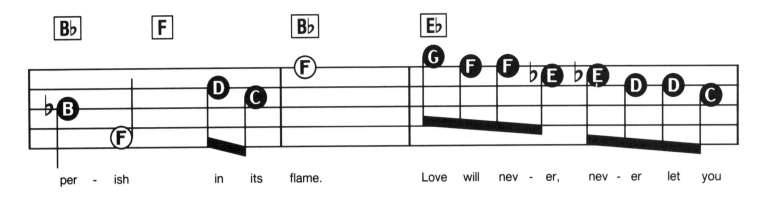

per - ish   in its   flame.   Love will nev - er, nev - er let you

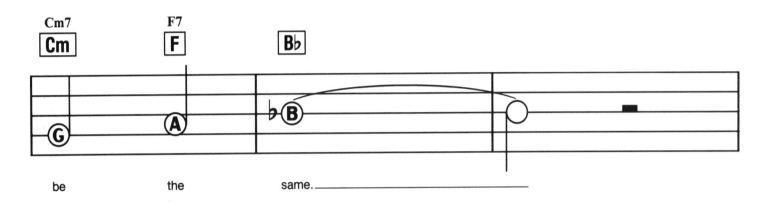

be   the   same.

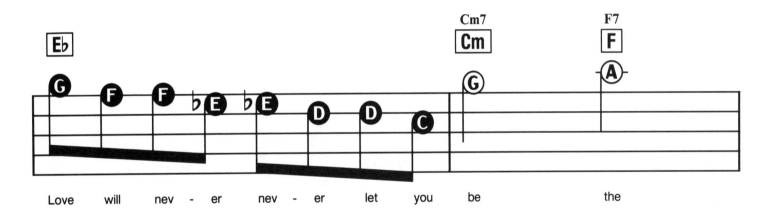

Love   will   nev - er   nev - er   let   you   be   the

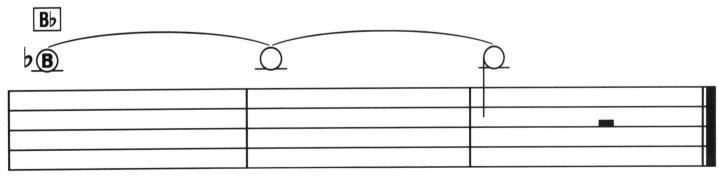

same.

Me and My Girl
from ME AND MY GIRL

Registration 2
Rhythm: Fox Trot or March

Words by Douglas Furber
Music by Noel Gay

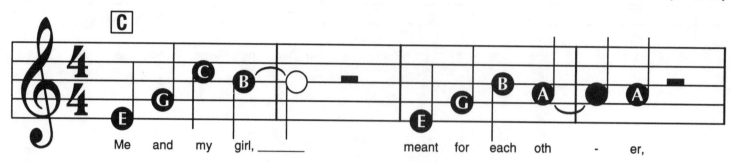

Me and my girl, _____ meant for each oth - er,

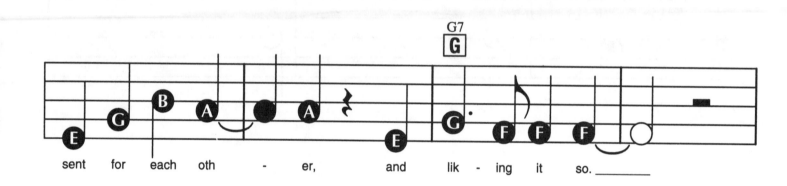

sent for each oth - er, and lik - ing it so. _____

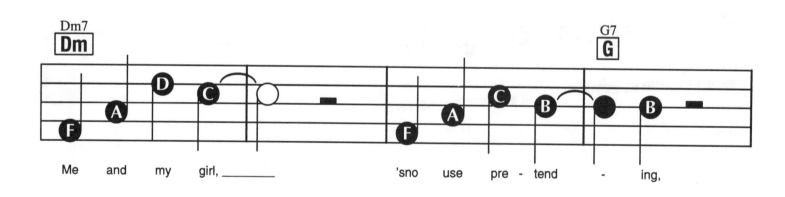

Me and my girl, _____ 'sno use pre - tend - ing,

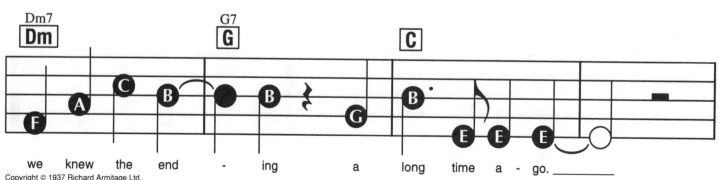

we knew the end - ing a long time a - go. _____

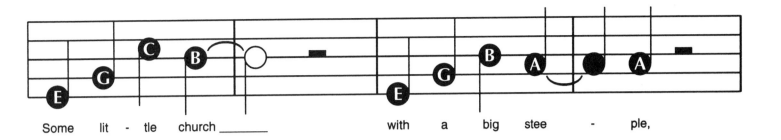

Some lit - tle church _____ with a big stee - ple,

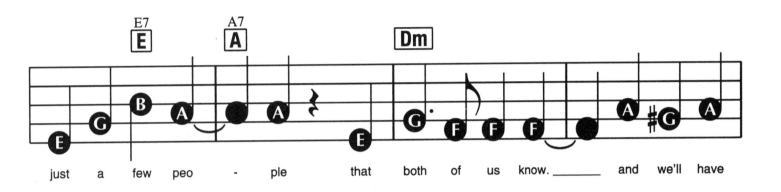

just a few peo - ple that both of us know. _____ and we'll have

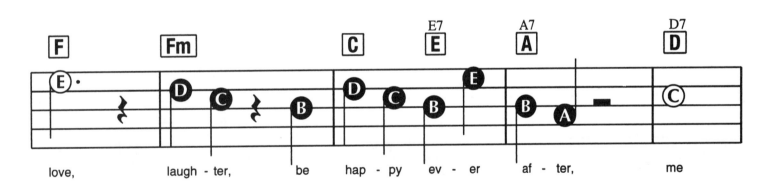

love, laugh - ter, be hap - py ev - er af - ter, me

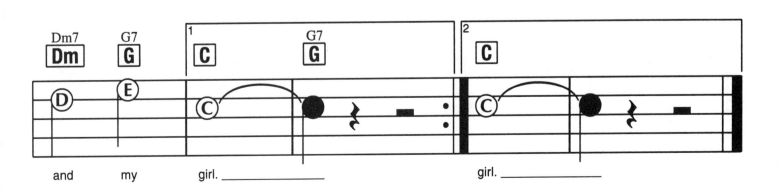

and my girl. _____ girl. _____

Oh, What a Beautiful Mornin'
from OKLAHOMA!

Registration 5
Rhythm: Waltz

Lyrics by Oscar Hammerstein II
Music by Richard Rodgers

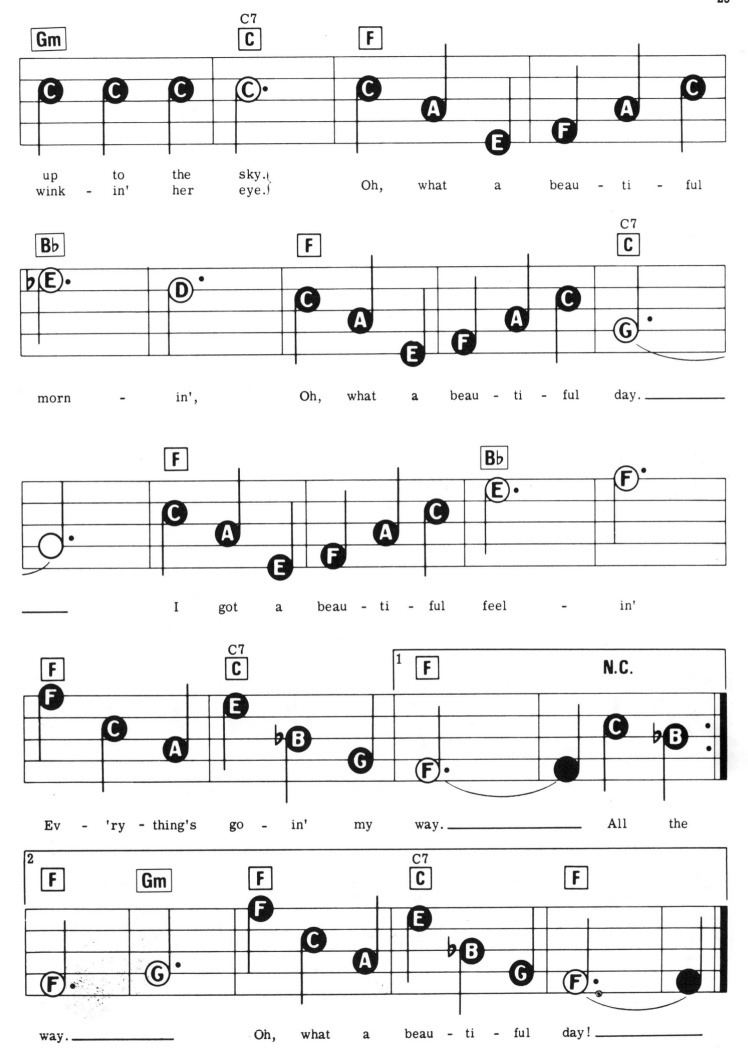

up to the sky.
wink - in' her eye.
Oh, what a beau - ti - ful

morn - in', Oh, what a beau - ti - ful day. _____

_____ I got a beau - ti - ful feel - in'

Ev - 'ry - thing's go - in' my way. _____ All the

way. _____ Oh, what a beau - ti - ful day! _____

Ol' Man River
from SHOW BOAT

Registration 5
Rhythm: Ballad or Fox Trot

Words by Oscar Hammerstein II
Music by Jerome Kern

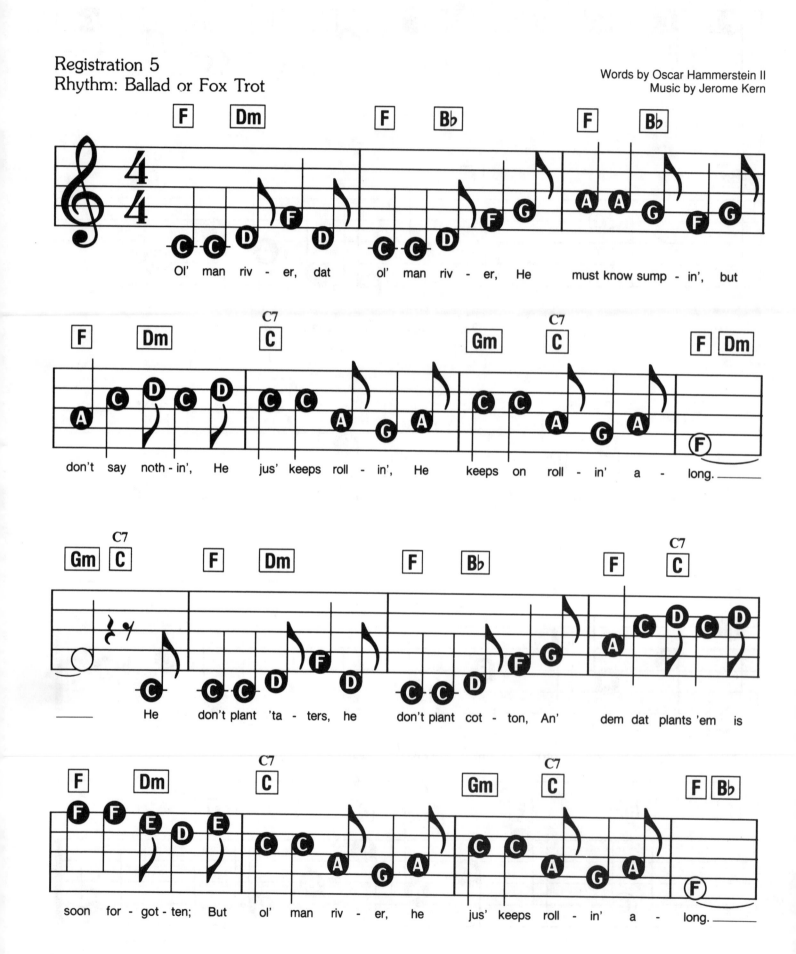

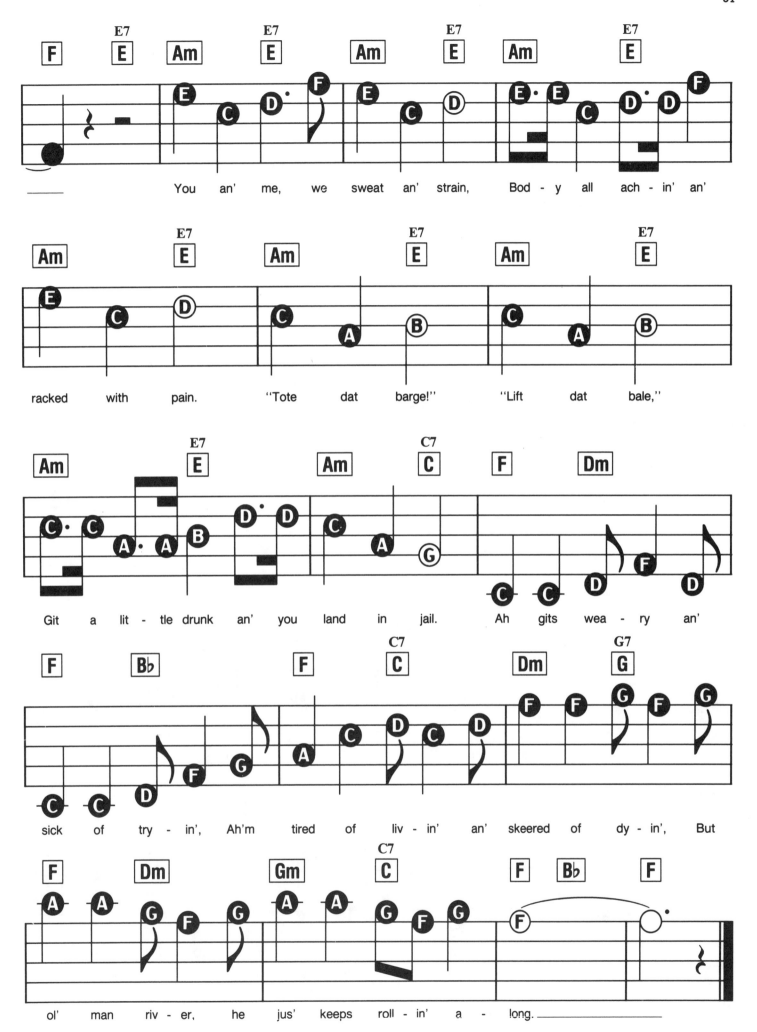

On My Own
from LES MISÉRABLES

Registration 1
Rhythm: Fox Trot or Ballad

Music by Claude-Michel Schönberg
Lyrics by Herbert Kretzmer, John Caird and Trevor Nunn
Original Text by Alain Boublil and Jean-Marc Natel

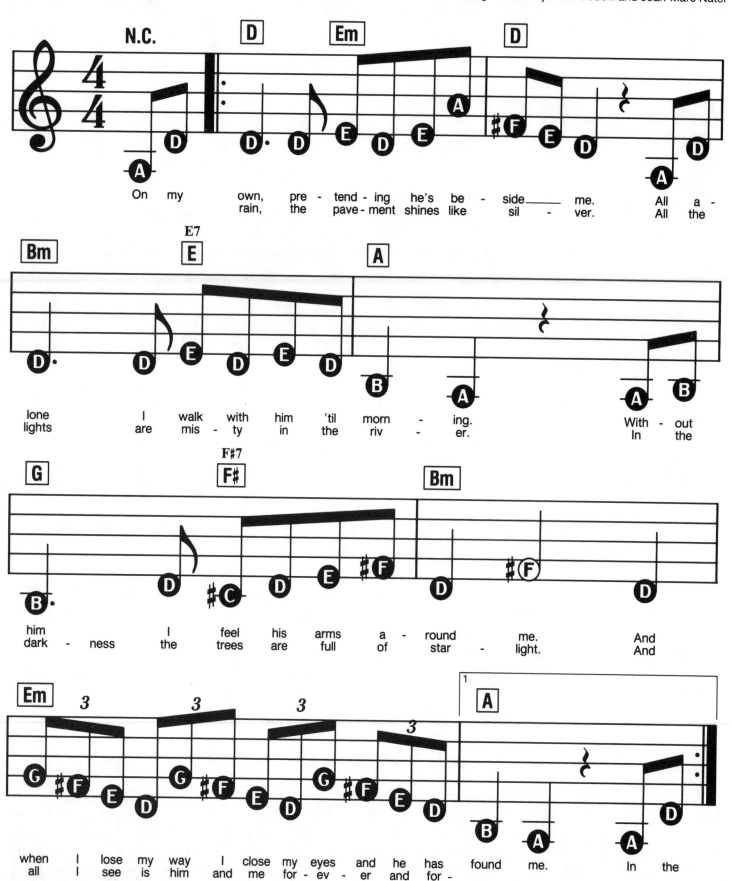

2

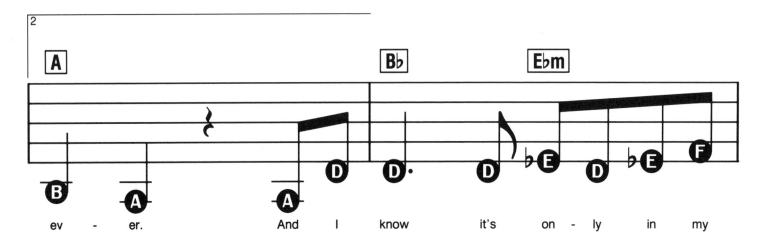

ev - er. And I know it's on - ly in my

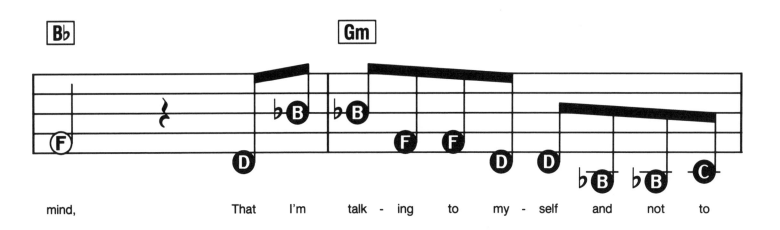

mind, That I'm talk - ing to my - self and not to

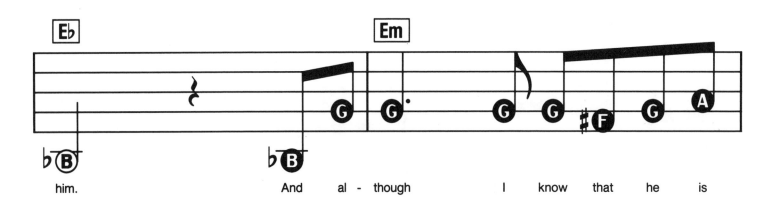

him. And al - though I know that he is

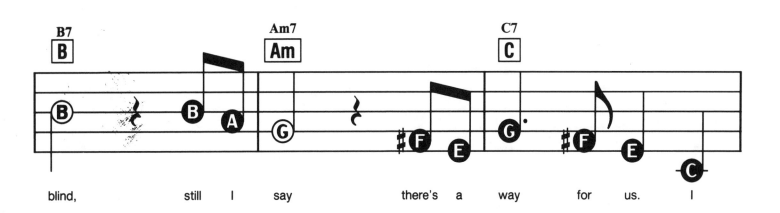

blind, still I say there's a way for us. I

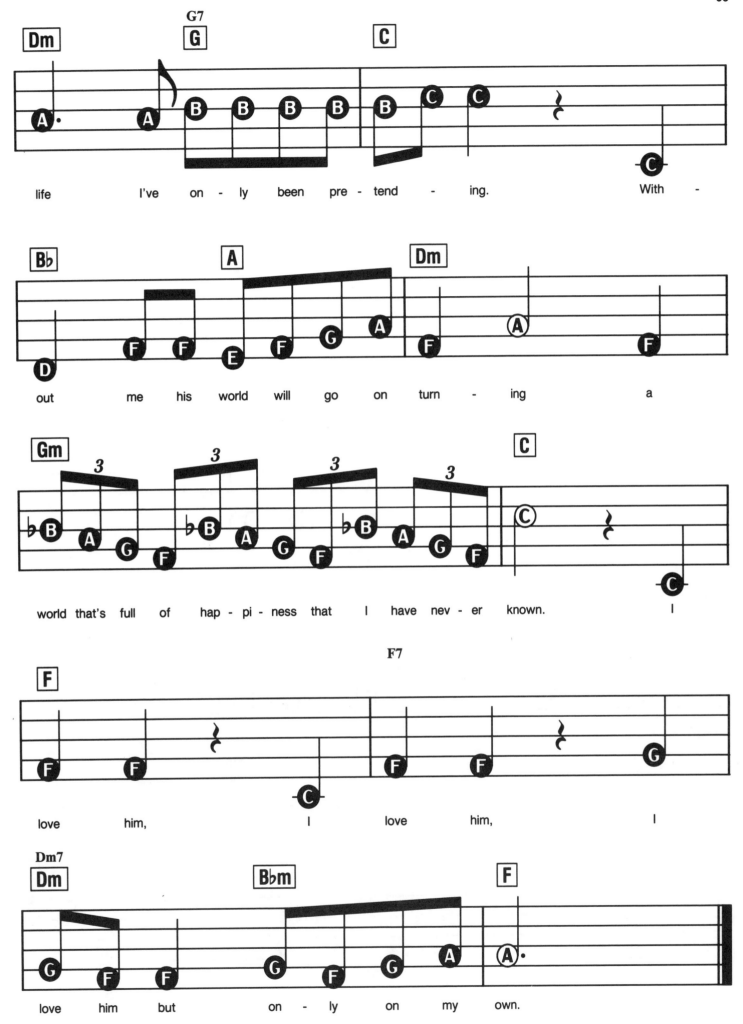

People Will Say We're in Love

from OKLAHOMA!

Registration 5
Rhythm: Fox Trot or Swing

Lyrics by Oscar Hammerstein II
Music by Richard Rodgers

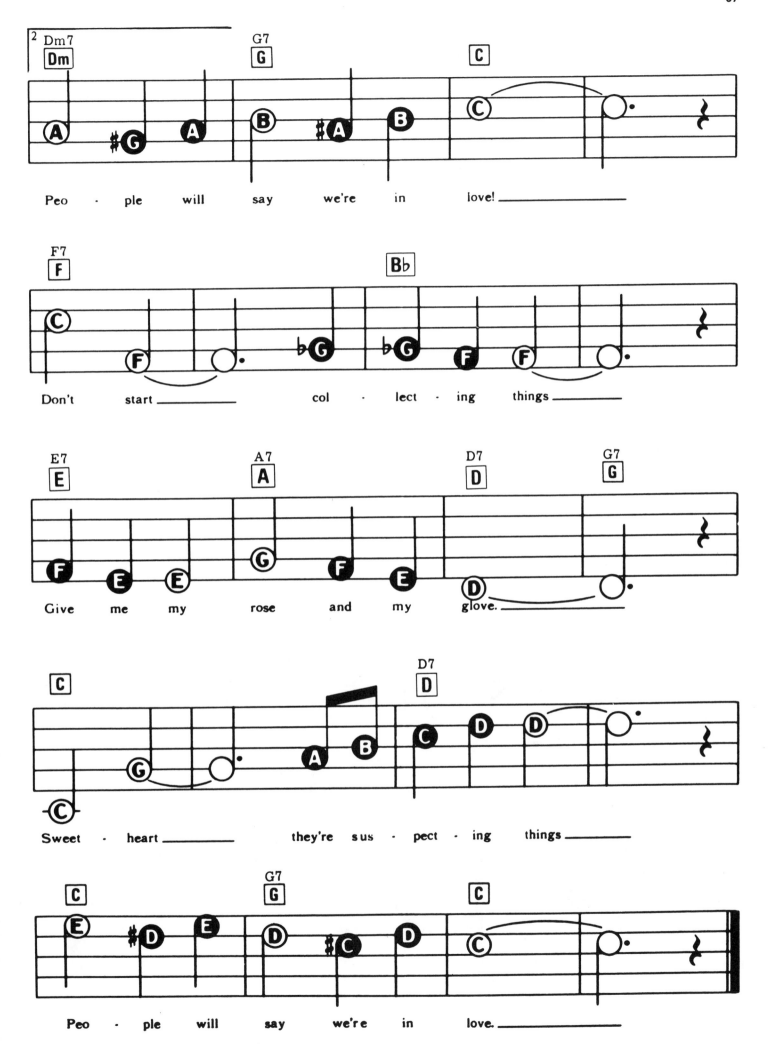

The Song Is You
from MUSIC IN THE AIR

Registration 5
Rhythm: Fox Trot or Swing

Words by Oscar Hammerstein II
Music by Jerome Kern

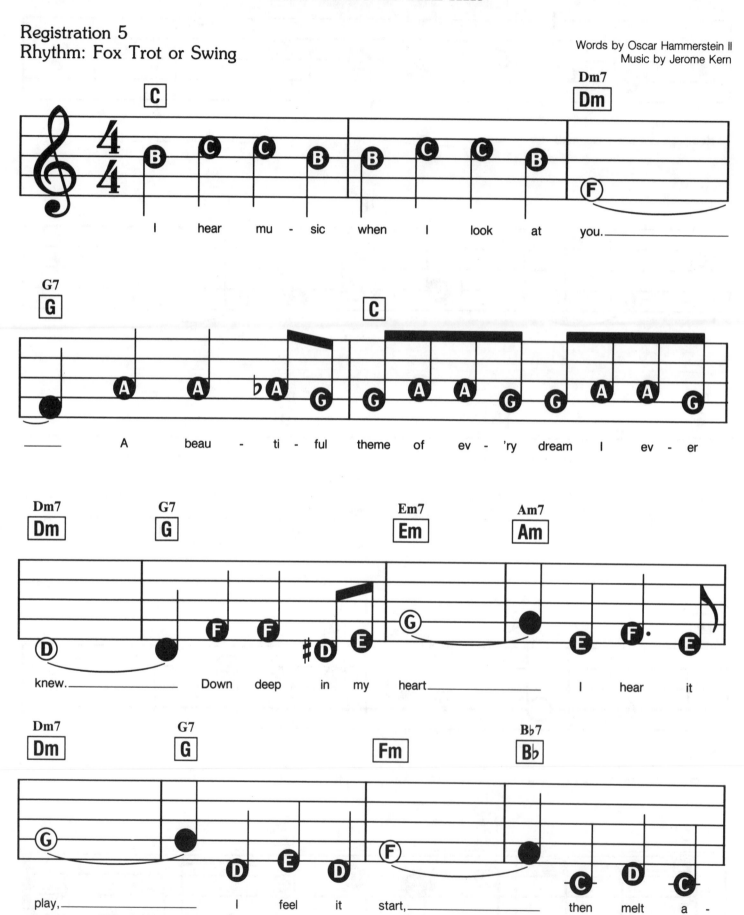

39

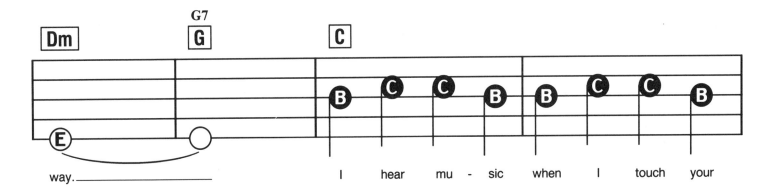

way._____ I hear mu - sic when I touch your

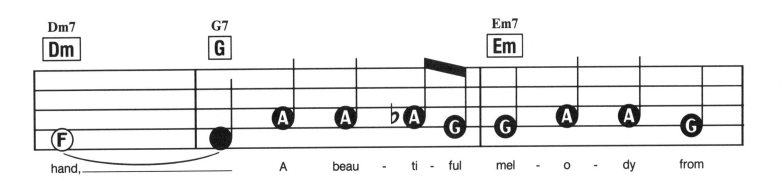

hand,_____ A beau - ti - ful mel - o - dy from

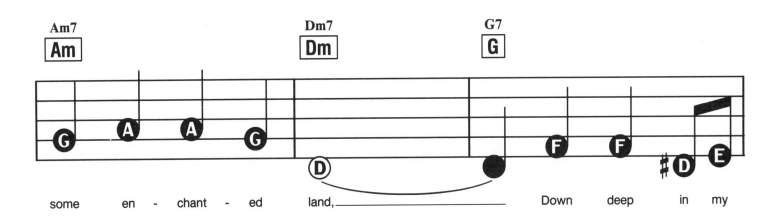

some en - chant - ed land,_____ Down deep in my

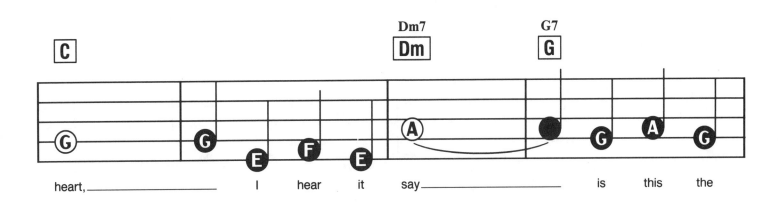

heart,_____ I hear it say_____ is this the

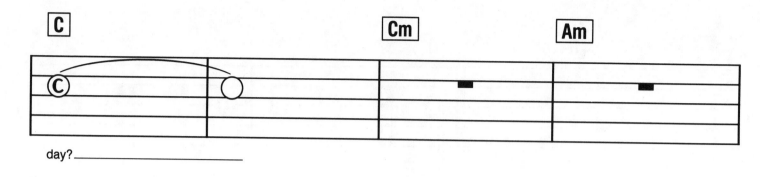

day?_____

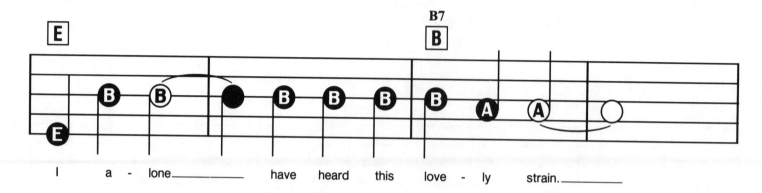

I a - lone_____ have heard this love - ly strain._____

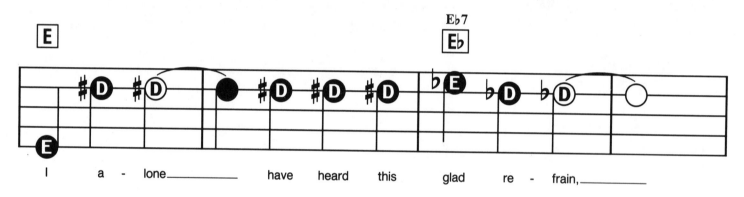

I a - lone_____ have heard this glad re - frain,_____

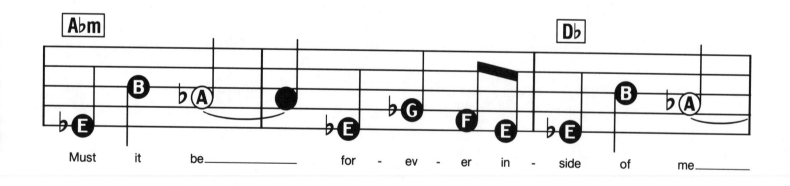

Must it be_____ for - ev - er in - side of me_____

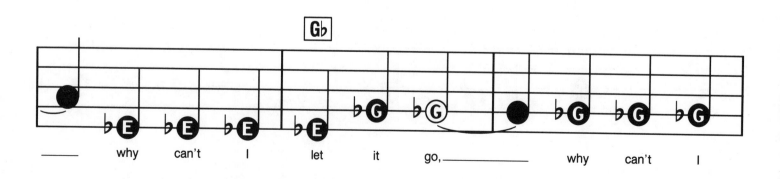

____ why can't I let it go,_____ why can't I

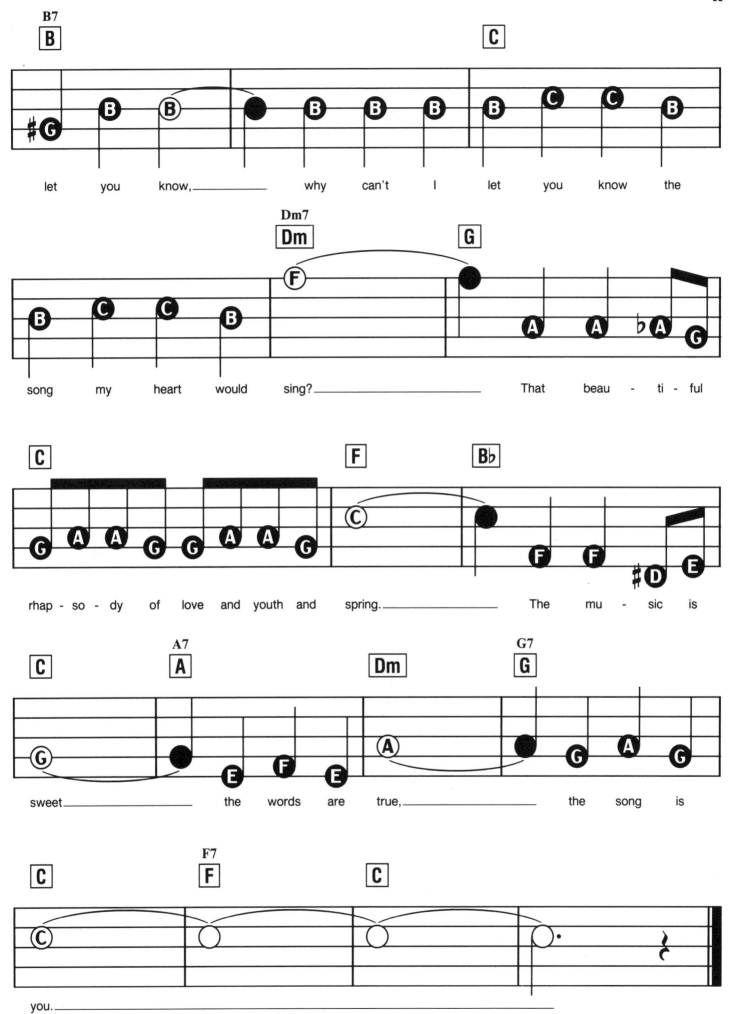

The Sound of Music
from THE SOUND OF MUSIC

Registration 5
Rhythm: Fox Trot

Lyrics by Oscar Hammerstein II
Music by Richard Rodgers

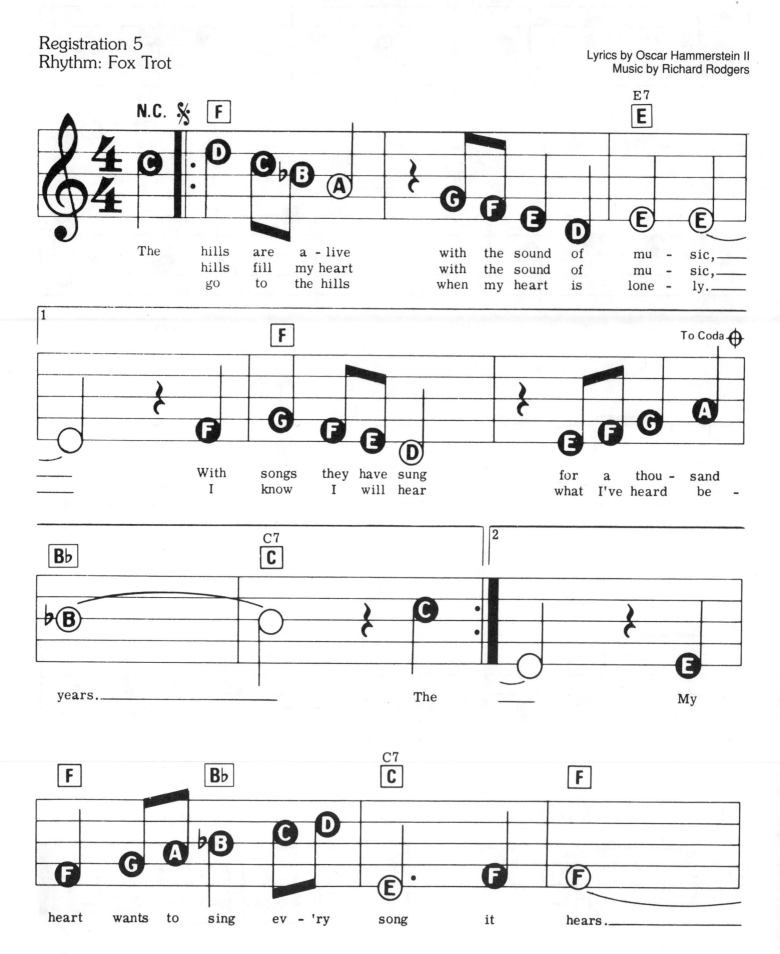

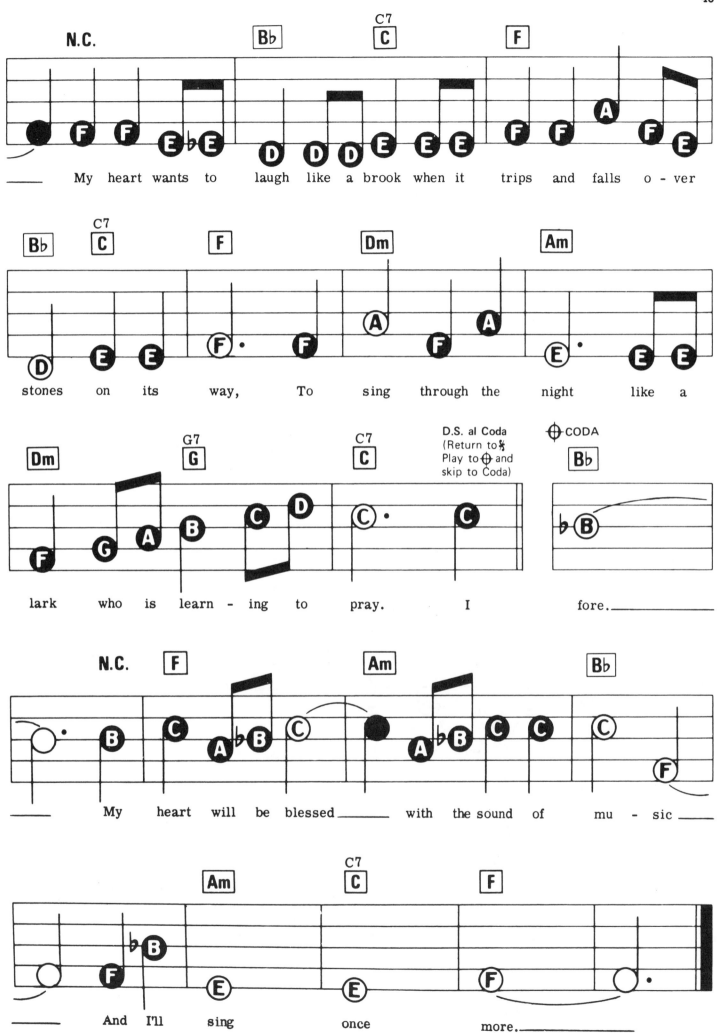

Sun and Moon
from MISS SAIGON

Registration 8
Rhythm: Pops or 8 Beat

Music by Claude-Michel Schönberg
Lyrics by Richard Maltby Jr. and Alain Boublil
Adapted from original French Lyrics by Alain Boublil

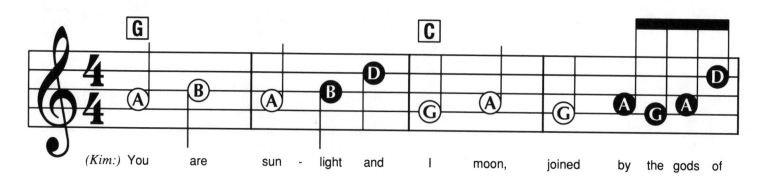

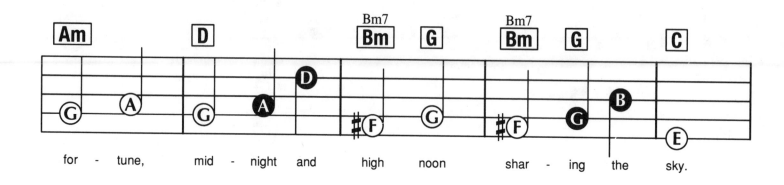

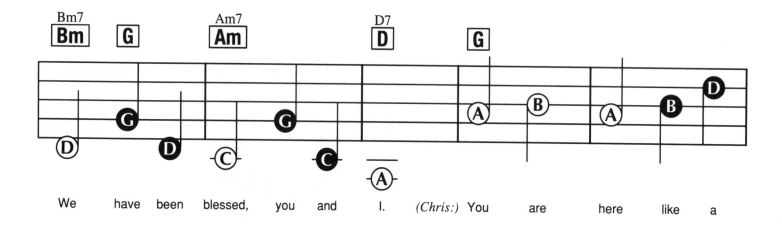

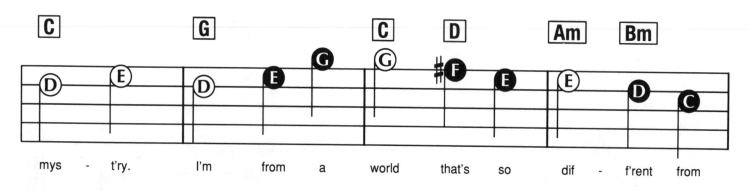

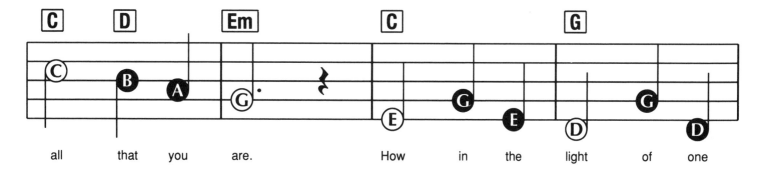

all that you are. How in the light of one

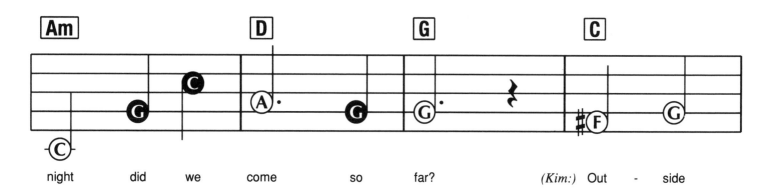

night did we come so far? *(Kim:)* Out - side

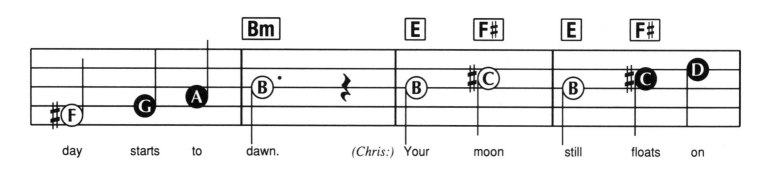

day starts to dawn. *(Chris:)* Your moon still floats on

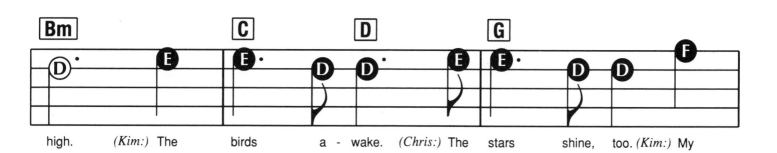

high. *(Kim:)* The birds a - wake. *(Chris:)* The stars shine, too. *(Kim:)* My

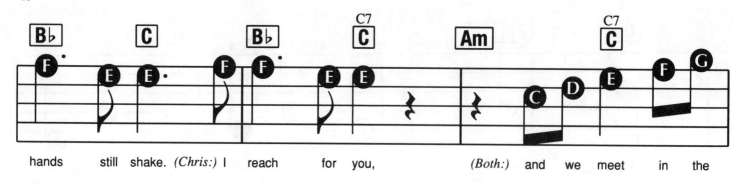

hands still shake. *(Chris:)* I reach for you, *(Both:)* and we meet in the

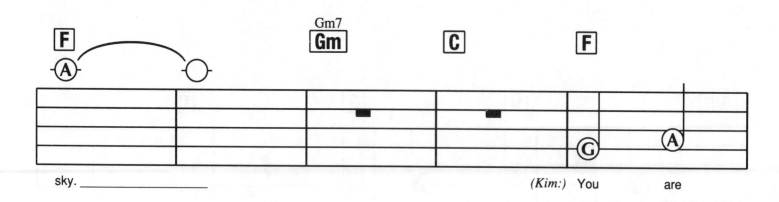

sky. _____ *(Kim:)* You are

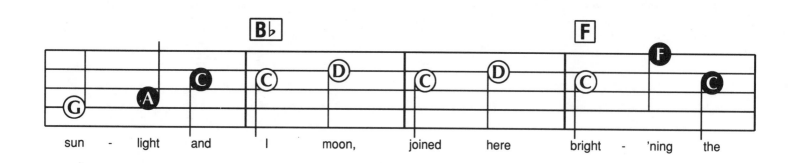

sun - light and I moon, joined here bright - 'ning the

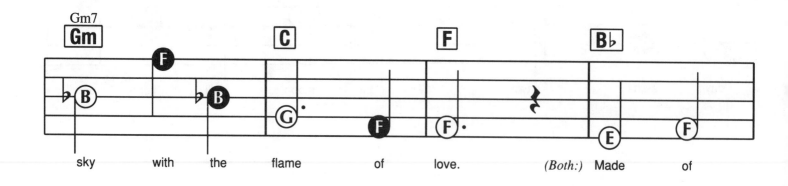

sky with the flame of love. *(Both:)* Made of

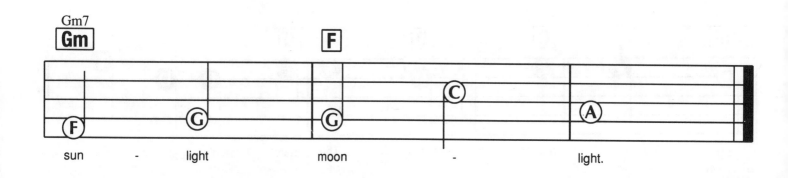

sun - light moon - light.

Superstar
from JESUS CHRIST SUPERSTAR

Registration: 9
Rhythm: Rock or Jazz Rock

Lyric by Tim Rice
Music by Andrew Lloyd Webber

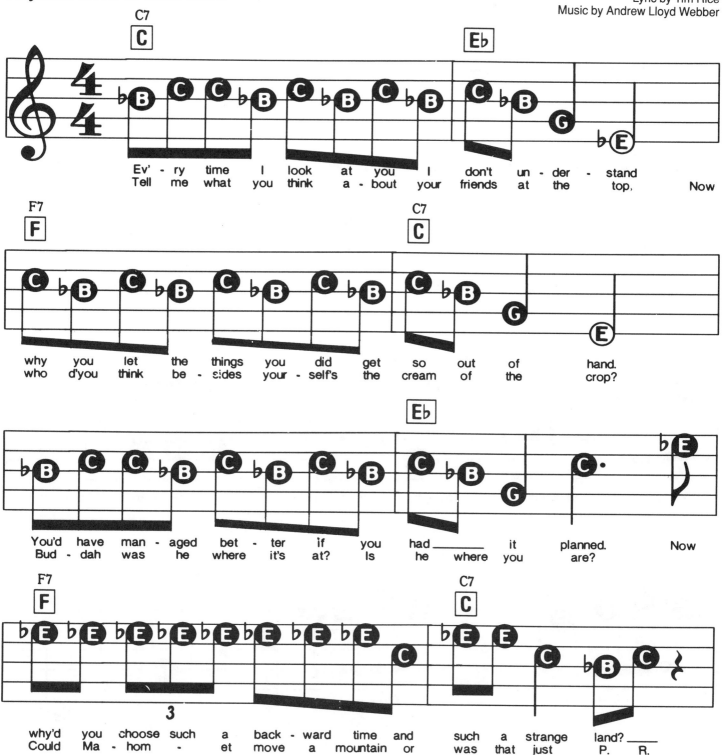

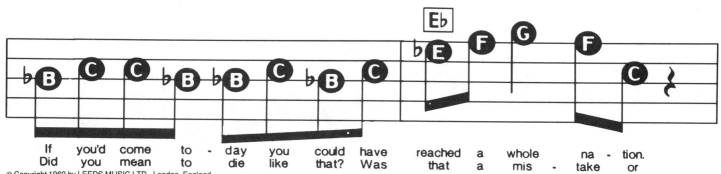

MCA music publishing

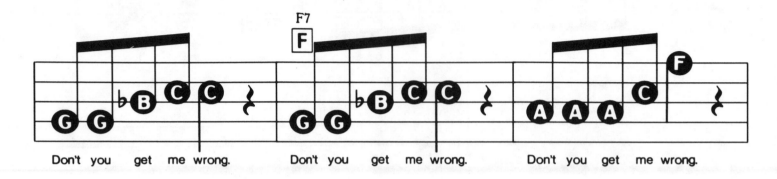

Is - rael in 4 B. C. had no mass com - mu - ni - ca - tion.
Did you know your mes - sy death would be a re - cord break - er?

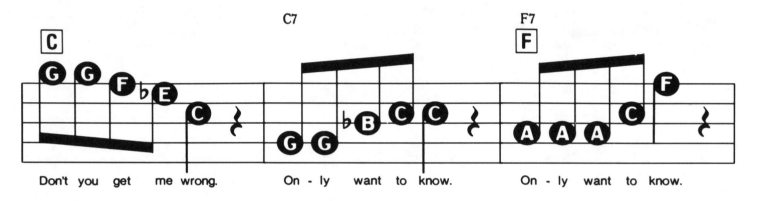

Don't you get me wrong. Don't you get me wrong. Don't you get me wrong.

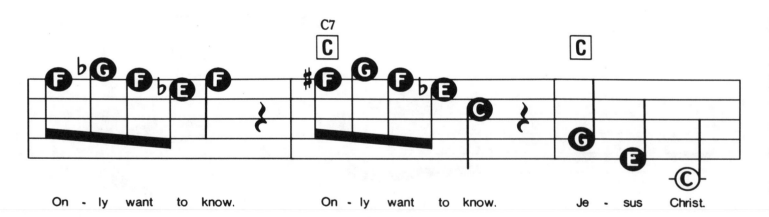

Don't you get me wrong. On - ly want to know. On - ly want to know.

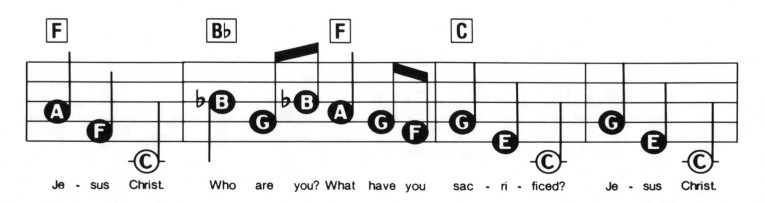

On - ly want to know. On - ly want to know. Je - sus Christ.

Je - sus Christ. Who are you? What have you sac - ri - ficed? Je - sus Christ.

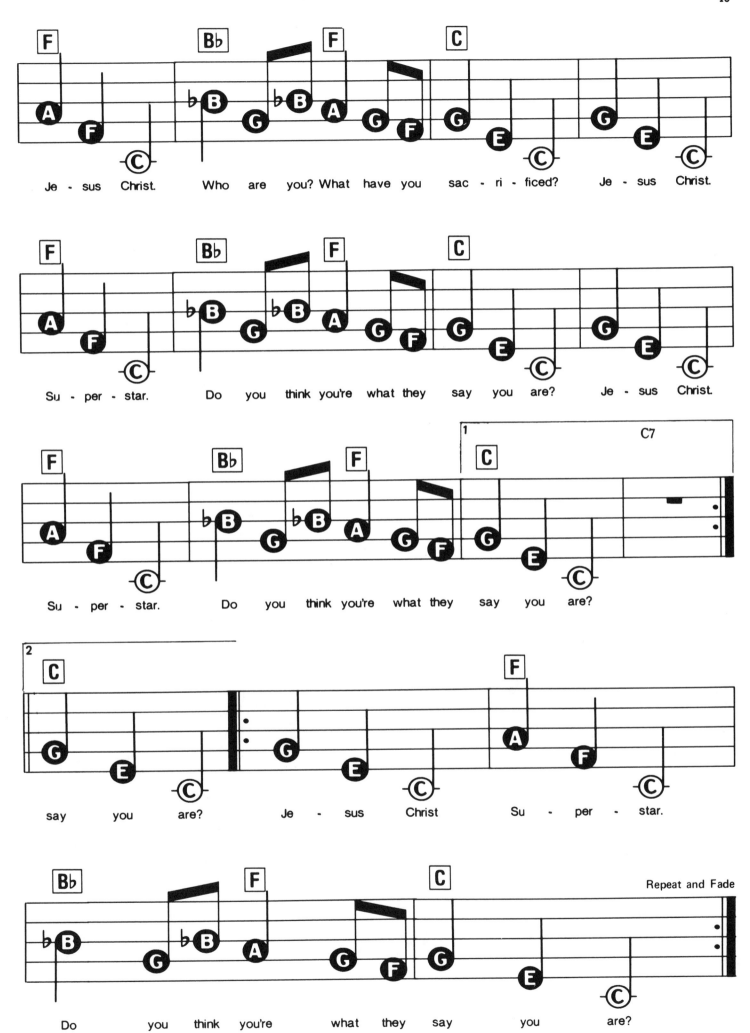

Till There Was You
from Meredith Willson's THE MUSIC MAN

Registration 2
Rhythm: Ballad

By Meredith Willson

There were bells on the hill, but I nev - er heard them

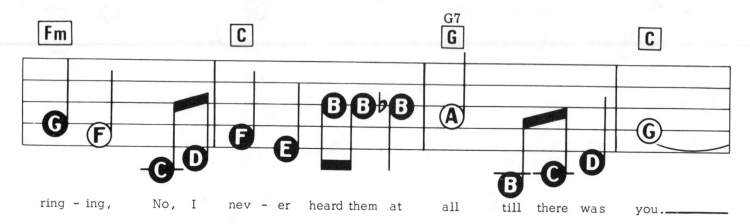

ring - ing, No, I nev - er heard them at all till there was you.

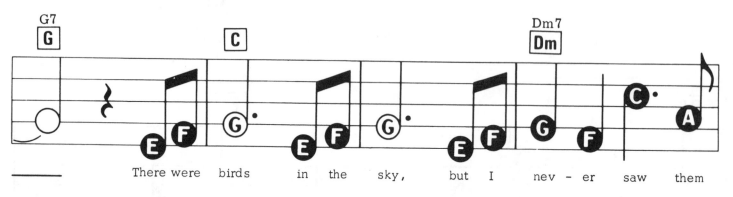

There were birds in the sky, but I nev - er saw them

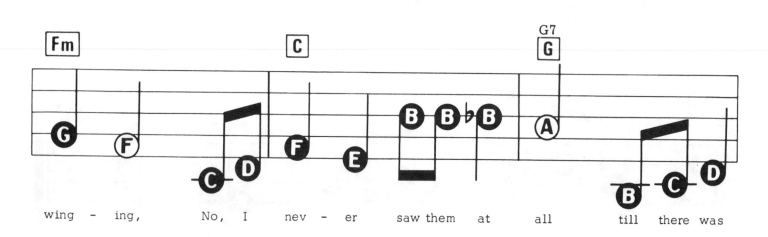

wing - ing, No, I nev - er saw them at all till there was

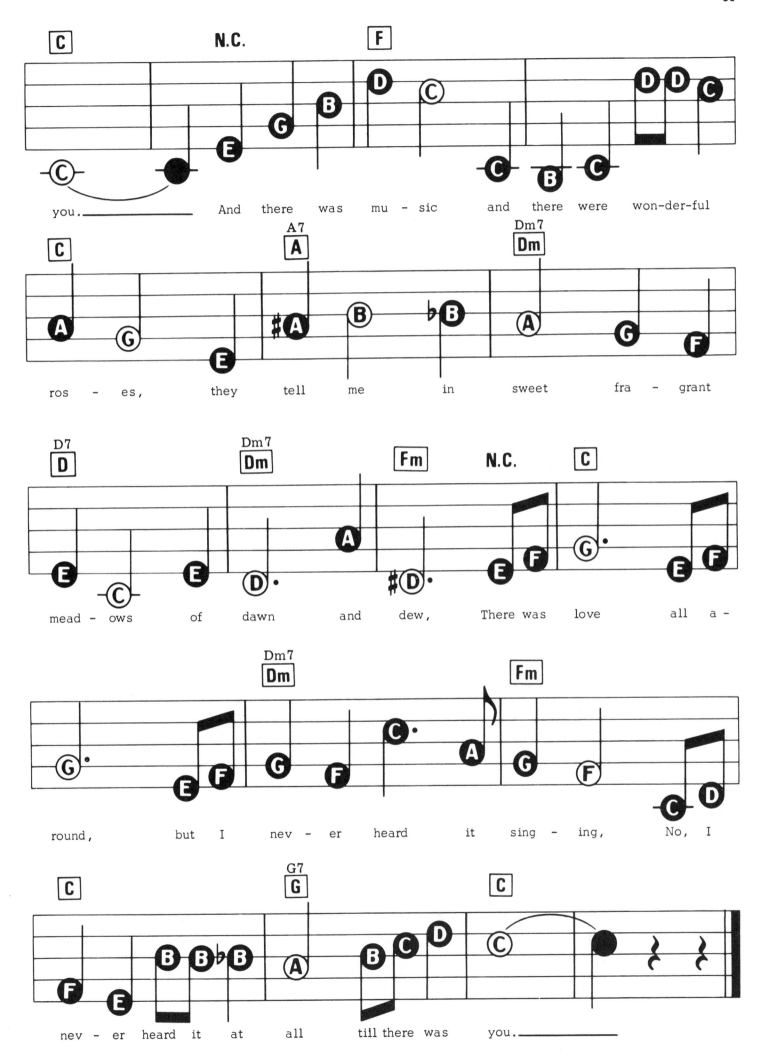

Unexpected Song
from SONG & DANCE

Registration 1
Rhythm: Rock or 8 Beat

Music by Andrew Lloyd Webber
Lyrics by Don Black

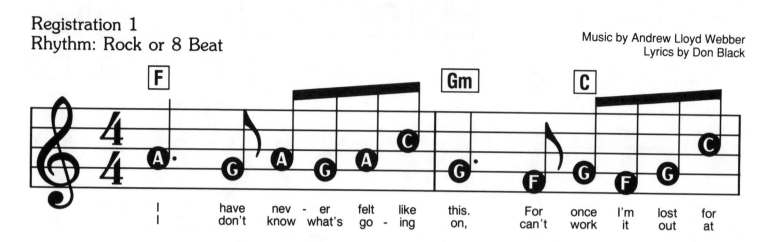

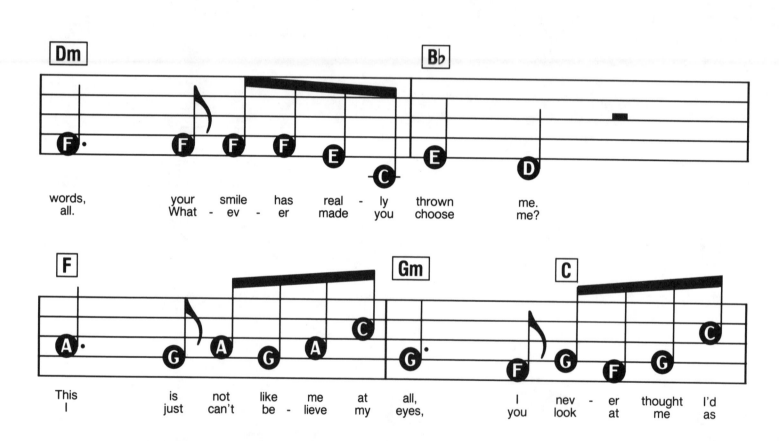

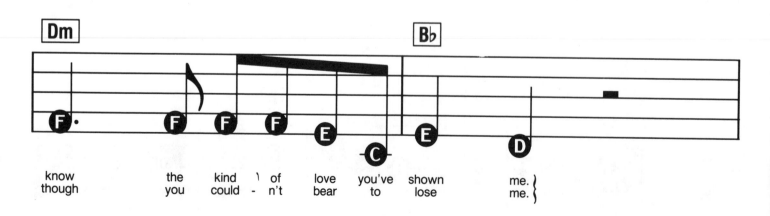

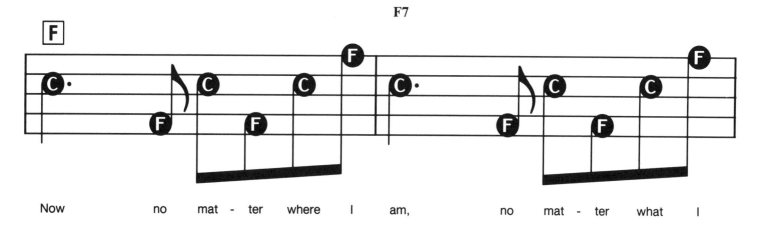

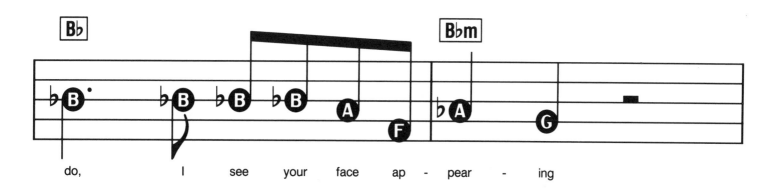

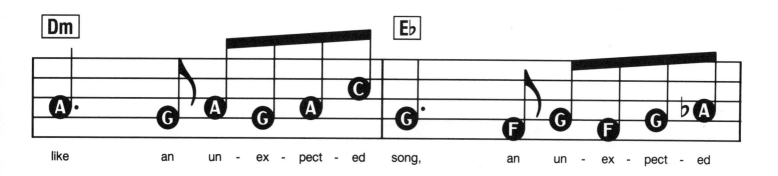

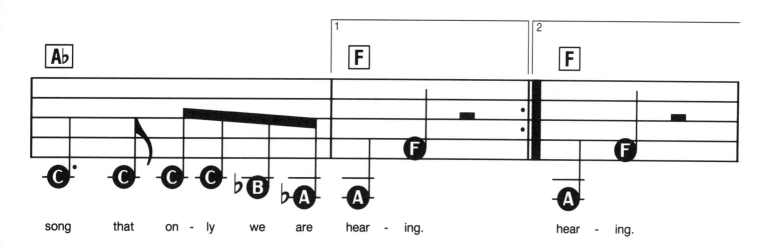

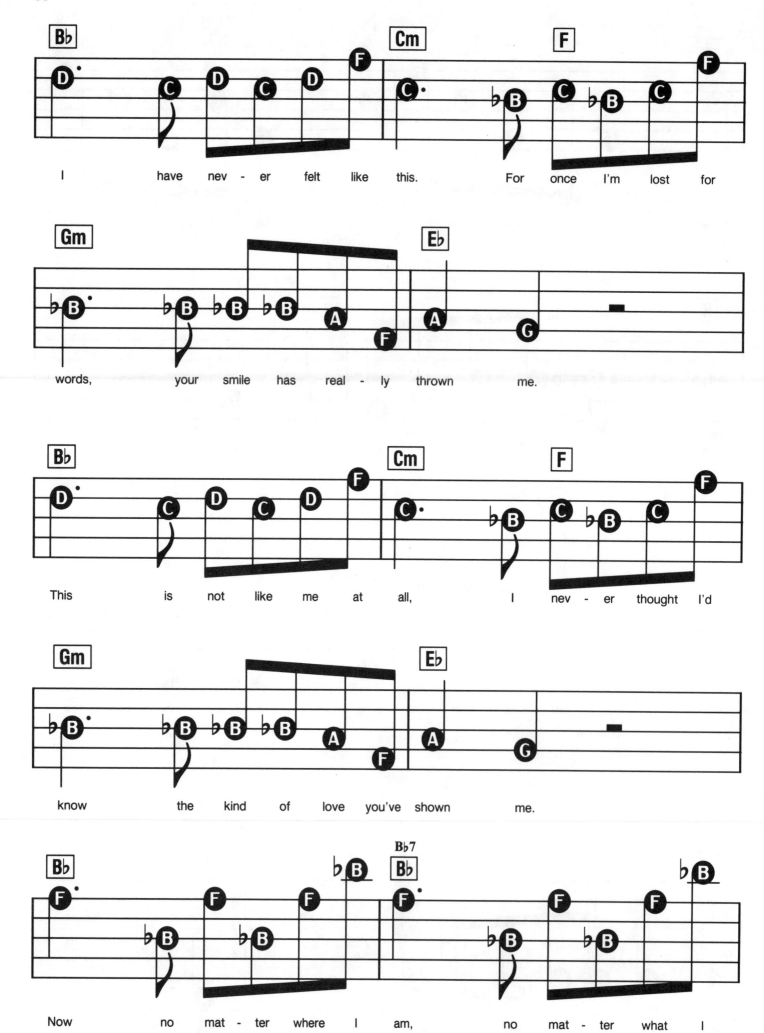

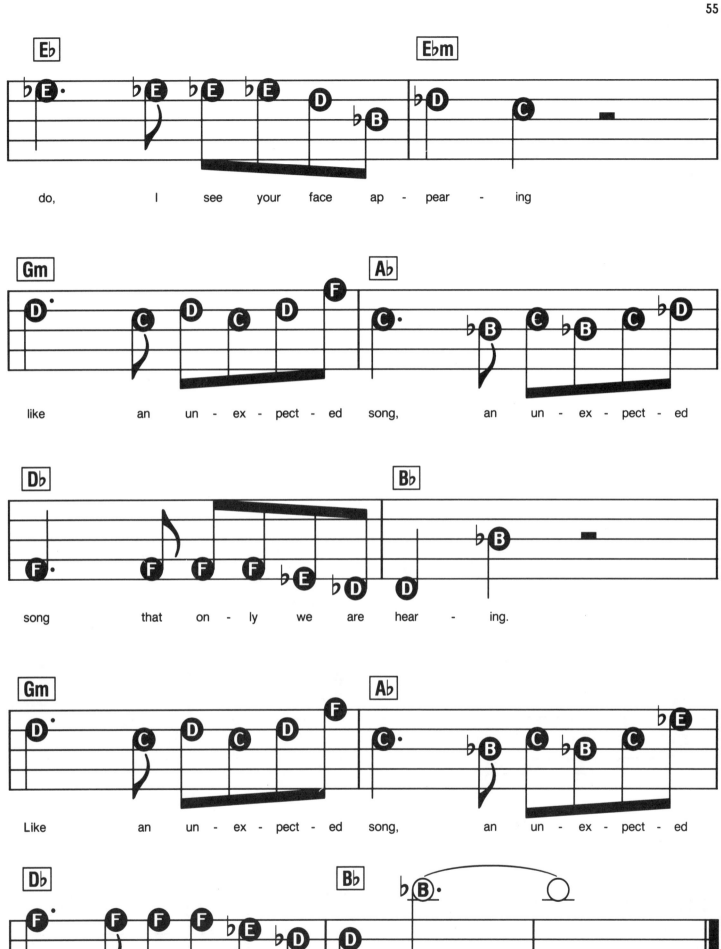

We Kiss in a Shadow
from THE KING AND I

Lyrics by Oscar Hammerstein II
Music by Richard Rodgers

Registration 2
Rhythm: Fox Trot or Ballad

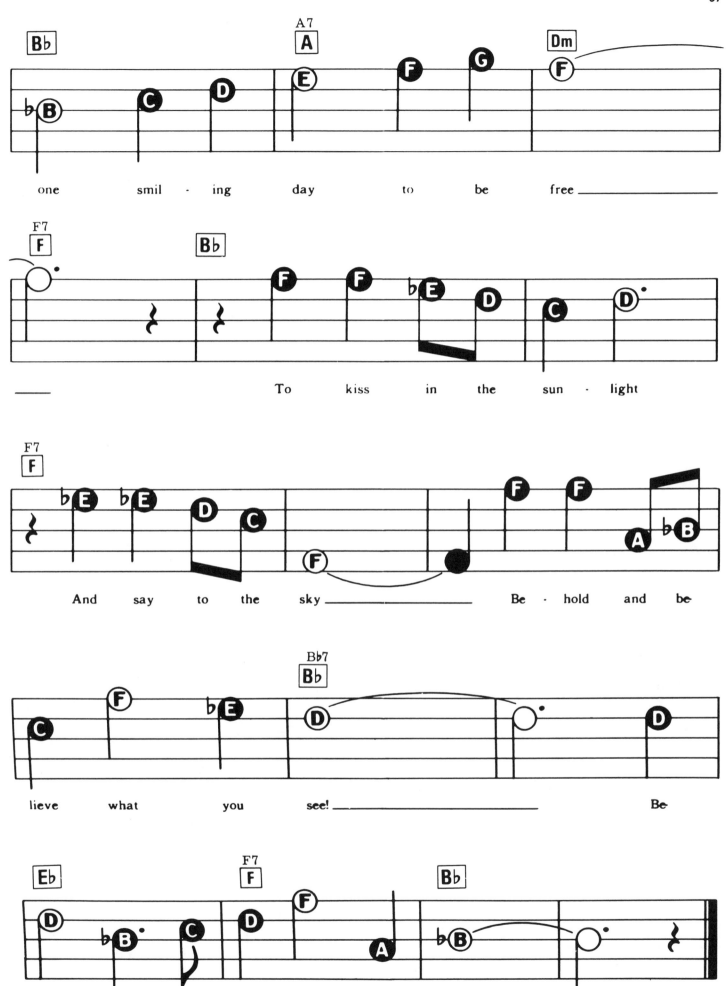

What Kind of Fool Am I?

from the Musical Production STOP THE WORLD - I WANT TO GET OFF

Registration 2
Rhythm: Fox Trot

Words and Music by Leslie Bricusse
and Anthony Newley

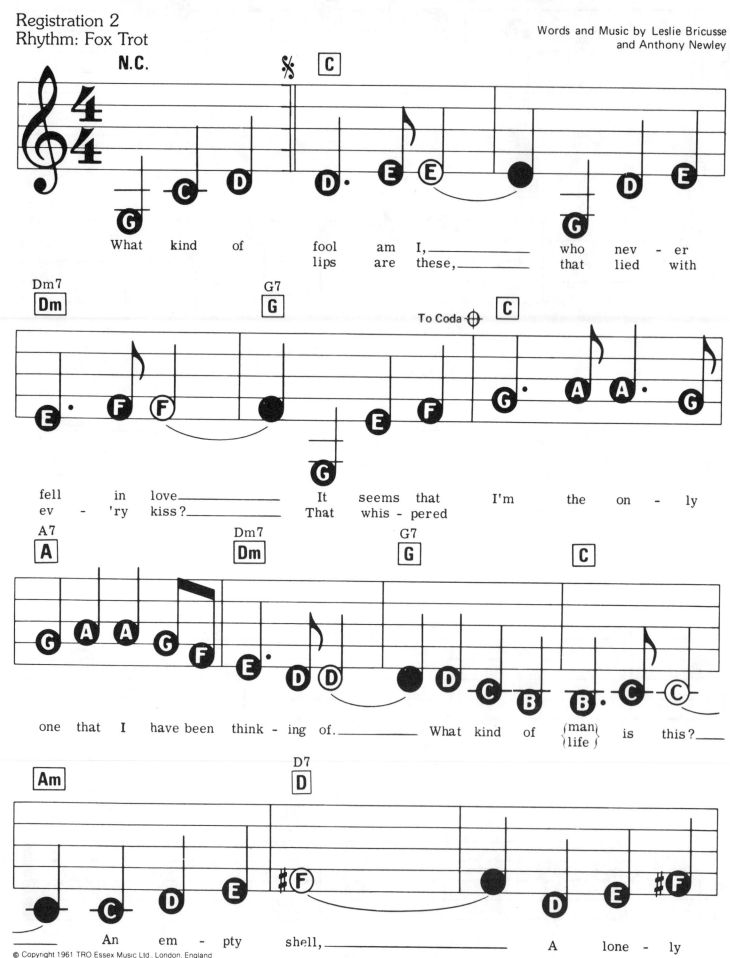

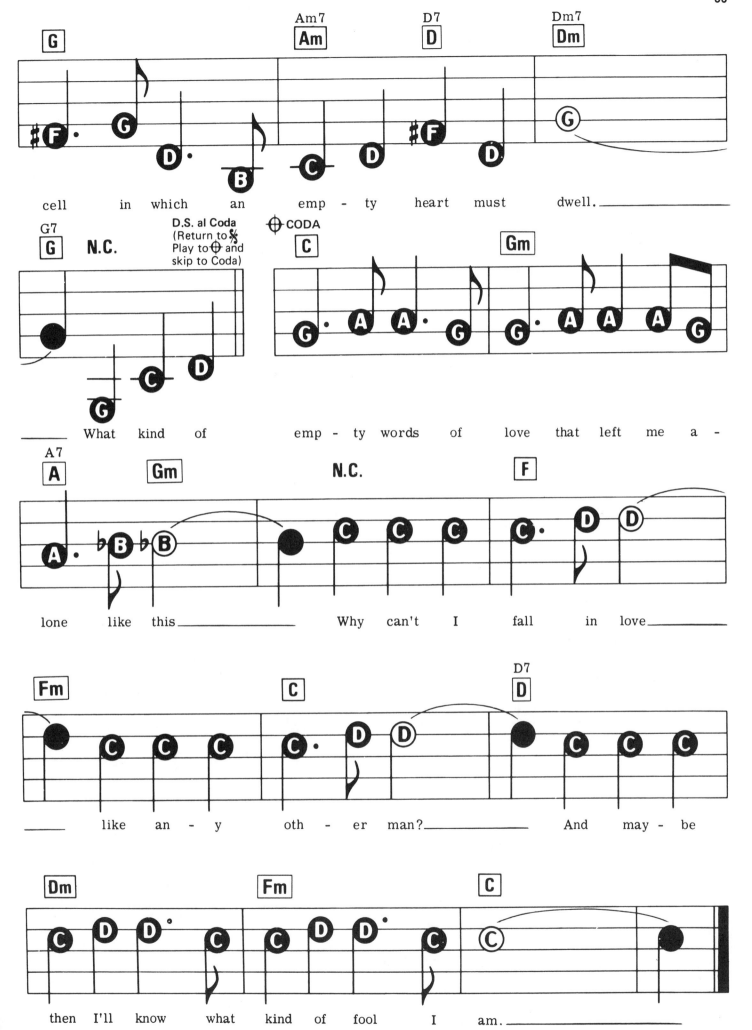

Why Do I Love You?

from SHOW BOAT

Registration 3
Rhythm: Fox Trot or Swing

Words by Oscar Hammerstein II
Music by Jerome Kern

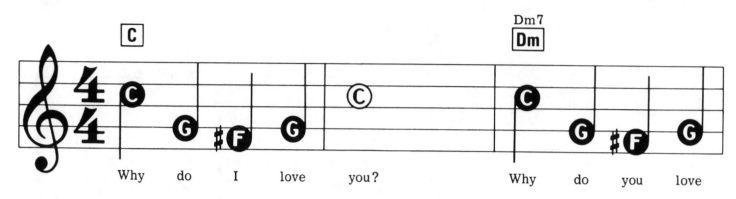

Why do I love you? Why do you love

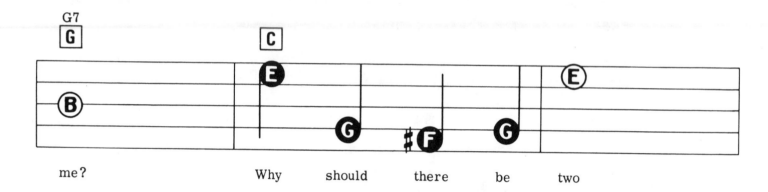

me? Why should there be two

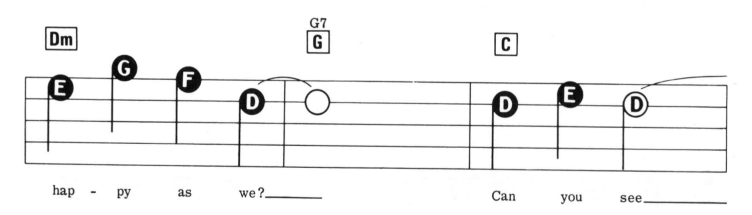

hap - py as we?_____ Can you see_____

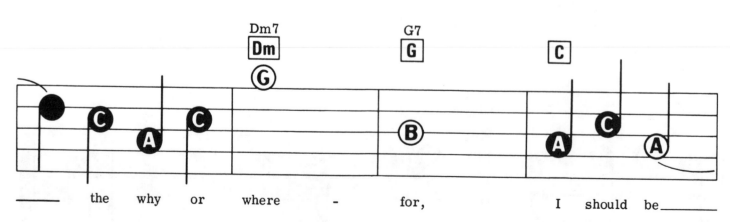

_____ the why or where - for, I should be_____

61

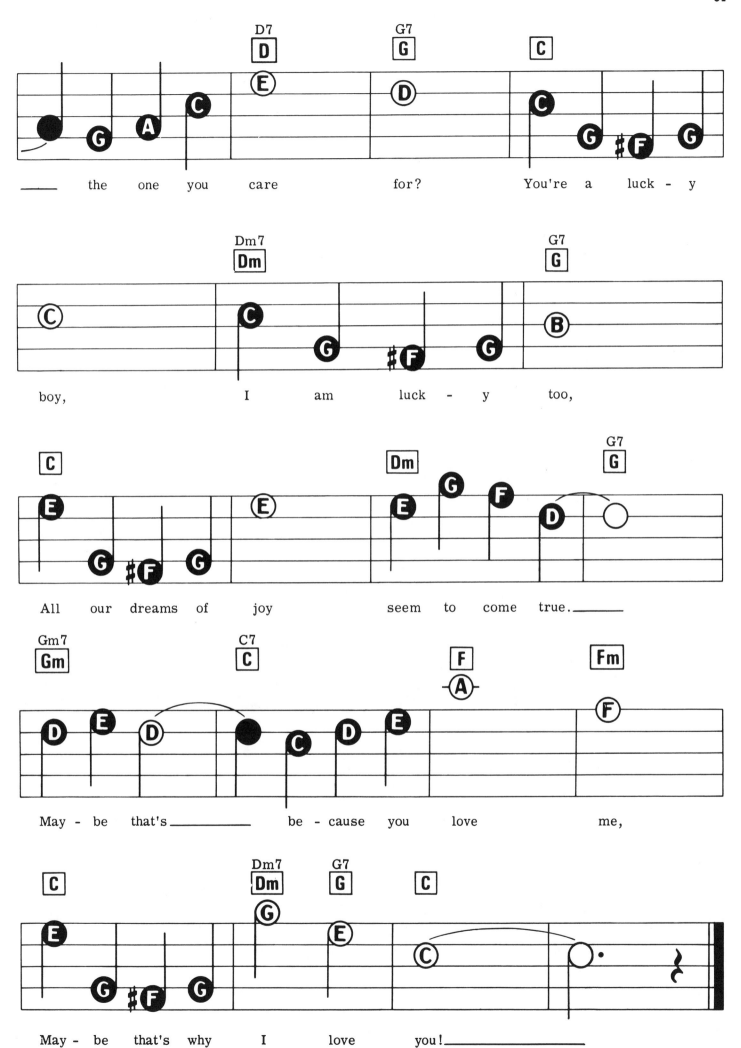

Younger than Springtime

from SOUTH PACIFIC

Registration 4
Rhythm: Fox Trot or Swing

Lyrics by Oscar Hammerstein II
Music by Richard Rodgers

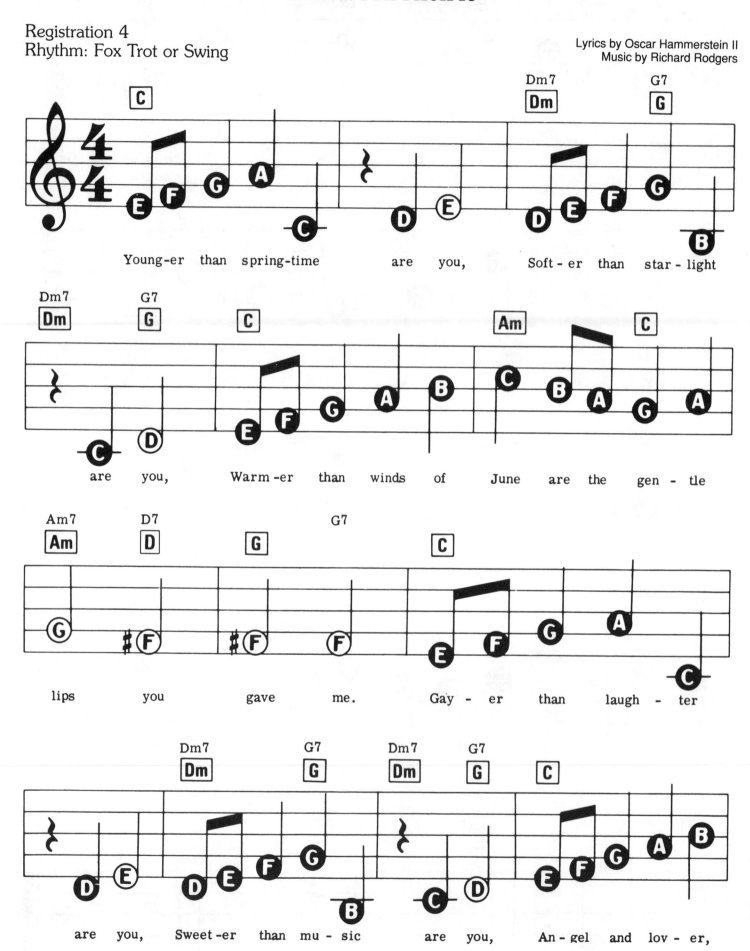

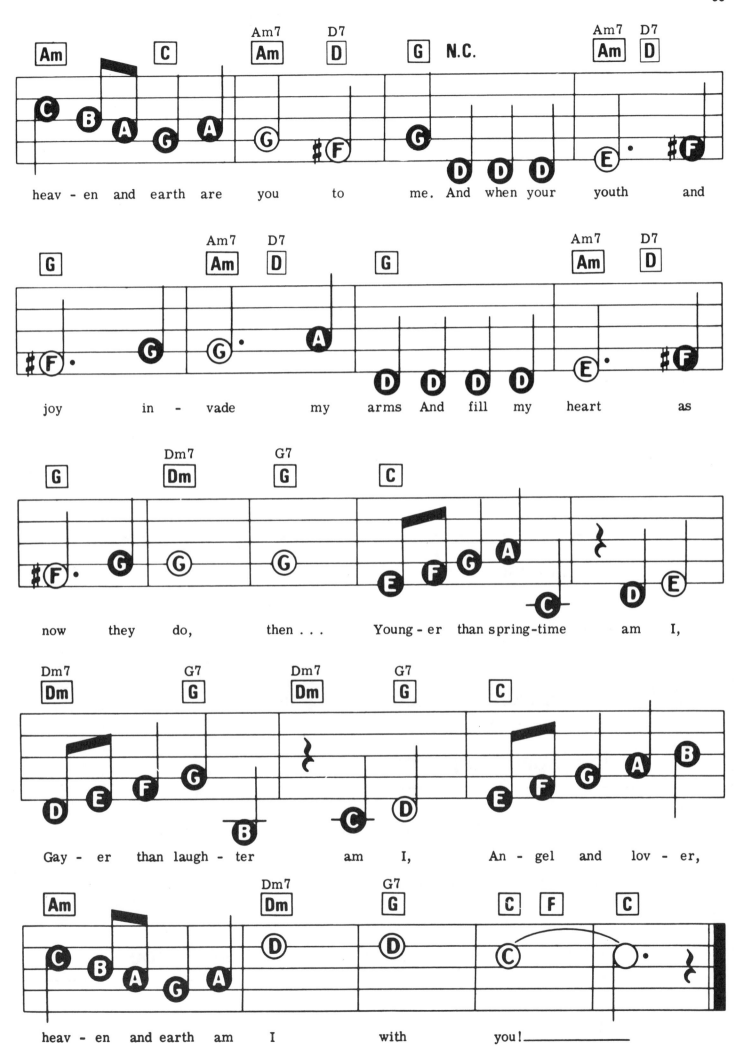

Registration Guide

- Match the Registration number on the song to the corresponding numbered category below. Select and activate an instrumental sound available on your instrument.

- Choose an automatic rhythm appropriate to the mood and style of the song. (Consult your Owner's Guide for proper operation of automatic rhythm features.)

- Adjust the tempo and volume controls to comfortable settings.

Registration

1	Flute, Pan Flute, Jazz Flute
2	Clarinet, Organ
3	Violin, Strings
4	Brass, Trumpet
5	Synth Ensemble, Accordion, Brass
6	Pipe Organ, Harpsichord
7	Jazz Organ, Vibraphone, Vibes, Electric Piano, Jazz Guitar
8	Piano, Electric Piano
9	Trumpet, Trombone, Clarinet, Saxophone, Oboe
10	Violin, Cello, Strings